PLASTICITY
IN ENGINEERING

BY

F. K. Th. van ITERSON

Former Professor of Applied Mechanics, Delft
Former Director of the Dutch State Mines

BLACKIE & SON LIMITED
LONDON AND GLASGOW

THIS BOOK IS PRODUCED IN COMPLETE
COMFORMITY WITH THE AUTHORIZED
ECONOMY STANDARDS

First published 1947

Printed in Great Britain by Blackie & Son, Ltd., Glasgow

PREFACE

As a basis for scientific engineering, mechanical as well as mining, the theory of plasticity is at least as important as the theory of elasticity, and a book on this branch of applied mechanics will further its more general use.

This is my excuse for writing a small textbook on plasticity.

The theory of elasticity reveals the occurrence of excessive stresses at re-entrant dihedral angles, especially at cracks in parts of structures, but the ductility of the steel lessens the danger of rupture, at least under static loading. It is often accepted without proof that the metal gives way at points where the yield stress is reached. The theory of plasticity for plane problems shows us that the stress must be as much as 2·57 times this value at a crack.

Experiments were needed to test the theory of plasticity both on notched bars and on thick-walled cylinders with a square boring. The laboratory of the State Mines and the High-Pressure Laboratory of the University of Amsterdam contributed to these costly investigations, which clarified the behaviour of mild steel, especially when rupturing at the strain limit. Soon it became clear that the axial principal stress plays a part in cases of two-dimensional strain, but the determination of its magnitude was not easy. New difficulties arose on the formulation of the laws of three-dimensional plastic flow. It became clear that these could not be solved in the study without the aid of laboratory investigation. Experiments made on the flow of clay at the pottery " De Sphinx " works at Maastricht brought forth a new conception of the plastic state of matter, which I was bold enough to call the fourth state of aggregation. It is situated between the solid and liquid states. Indeed, when the flow in one principal direction is impeded, two principal stresses become equal, not all

v

three as in the liquid state. In this condition the material flows in the direction in which it can escape, but solidifies as soon as the principal stress difference drops.

To stimulate criticism I discussed my ideas in scientific and technical circles. This proved very helpful in moulding definite conceptions. Some mistakes pointed out by friends have been corrected.

v. I.

THE HAGUE, HOLLAND,
        1947.

CONTENTS

CHAP.   Page

I.   THE EQUILIBRIUM OF INTERNAL STRESSES AND PLASTICITY.
      TWO-DIMENSIONAL OR PLANE PROBLEMS   -   -   -   1

II.   THE THICK-WALLED CYLINDER   -   -   -   -   -   10

III. THE THEOREM OF HENCKY AND THE PLASTIC SECTOR   -   -   15

IV.   THE SOLUTION OF PLASTICITY PROBLEMS BY MEANS OF THE
      PLASTIC SECTOR   -   -   -   -   -   -   -   19

V.   PLASTIC DEFORMATION AT SHARP GROOVES   -   -   -   26

VI.   THE PLASTIC MASS COMPRESSED BETWEEN PARALLEL PLANES   40

VII. THE PLASTIC MASS COMPRESSED BETWEEN INCLINED PLANES -   49

VIII. THE OUTER REGIONS OF PLASTIC DEFORMATION IN THE MASS
      COMPRESSED BETWEEN PARALLEL PLANES   -   -   -   56

IX.   THE PLASTIFICATION IN THE ANNULAR SPACE BETWEEN TWO
      CONCENTRIC CYLINDERS, CAUSED BY RELATIVE TRANSLATION.
      CLAY-CUTTING WITH A WIRE   -   -   -   -   -   59

X.   THREE-DIMENSIONAL PLASTICITY   -   -   -   -   -   63

XI.   THE IDEAL YIELD STRESS   -   -   -   -   -   -   76

XII. THE THICK-WALLED SPHERE AND WIRE-DRAWING   -   -   -   81

XIII. ON THE TENDENCY OF THE MEAN PRINCIPAL STRESS TO EQUAL
      EITHER THE GREATEST PRINCIPAL STRESS OR THE SMALLEST   83

XIV. THE DISC PLASTOMETER   -   -   -   -   -   -   86

XV.   THE BRINELL HARDNESS TEST   -   -   -   -   -   92

XVI. THE GROOVED CYLINDRICAL TEST BAR   -   -   -   102

XVII. PLASTIC TORSION   -   -   -   -   -   -   -   109

XVIII. DO SLIP PLANES OCCUR IN PLASTIC FLOW?   -   -   -   113

XIX. THE STRENGTHENING OF MILD STEEL BY WORK-HARDENING -   121

XX.   THE OCCURRENCE OF SO-CALLED BRITTLE RUPTURE IN PLASTIC
      MATERIAL   -   -   -   -   -   -   -   -   125

CONTENTS

CHAP.		Page
XXI.	THE THEORY OF RUPTURE - - - - - - -	131
XXII.	RUPTURE AT SHARP INCISIONS - - - - -	139
XXIII.	APPLICATIONS - - - - - - - -	146
XXIV.	PLASTIC FLEXURE - - - - - - -	163
	INDEX - - - - - - - -	171

NOTATION

PRINCIPAL STRESSES	s_1, s_2, s_3
NORMAL STRESS	s_n
SHEAR STRESS	s_s
AIRY'S STRESS FUNCTION	F
TENSILE YIELD LIMIT	s_0
SHEAR STRESS YIELD LIMIT	k
TANGENTIAL, RADIAL AND AXIAL STRESS	$s_t \ s_r, \ s_z$
POLAR CO-ORDINATES	r, ϕ
ANGLES BETWEEN TWO RADII OR **TWO** TANGENTS TO THE SAME CURVE	ϕ
TENSILE STRENGTH	R
TENSION OR FORCE PER CM.^{2}	p
SPECIFIC DEFORMATION	σ
ANGLE BETWEEN THE PRINCIPAL DIRECTIONS AND THE X- AND Y-AXIS	α
ANGLE BETWEEN THE MAXIMUM SHEAR STRESSES AND THE X- AND Y-AXIS	β
CHARACTERISTIC SHEAR STRESS	s_{sc}
IDEAL TENSILE STRESS	s_i
POISSON'S RATIO	$\dfrac{1}{m}$

The Equilibrium of Internal Stresses and Plasticity. Two-dimensional or Plane Problems

1. To understand the behaviour of loaded structures or machine parts, the engineer must take into account the deformation of the material at incisions, holes, pores and other danger spots where the limit of elasticity is exceeded. He must be familiar with the stresses existing under the conditions of plastic flow involved in wire-drawing, rolling, cutting, forging and pressing metals, in the manufacture of pipes or profiles by extrusion, in ball indentation and other ways of deforming or moulding plastic matter.

This textbook deals especially with three-dimensional strains, but to facilitate the study, we start with two-dimensional problems dealing with plastic bodies of uniform section enclosed between parallel end-planes, e.g. a clay dam between abutments. The special feature of plane problems is that there is no displacement normal to the section considered.

When a structural part is loaded till permanently deformed, flow will in general only have occurred at certain spots. In the cross-sections of plane problems, regions of plastic and elastic strain adjoin. We shall find that the boundaries are determined by the plastic flow. Stress and strain in parts of the section loaded below the elastic limit are less than in the regions of plastic deformation.

To solve problems on plasticity, we use the same equations of internal equilibrium of stresses as in problems on elasticity, but instead of the linear relation between strain and stress, we only use the so-called condition of plasticity which simplifies the theory.

Although most readers may pass on, for the sake of completeness we deduce the conditions for internal equilibrium.

At each point of the material under tension two perpendicular planes can be chosen, subject to normal tensions only. We call these planes *principal planes*, the normals to these planes the *principal directions*, and the normal stresses themselves the *principal stresses*, which we indicate by s_1 and s_2. The equilibrium of the forces on the sides of an elementary prism (fig. 1) in the direction of the normal on a plane which makes an angle α with the first principal plane gives the normal stress

$$s_n = s_1 \cos^2 \alpha + s_2 \sin^2 \alpha,$$

and the equilibrium of the forces in the tangential direction gives the tangential stress

$$s_s = s_1 \cos \alpha \sin \alpha - s_2 \sin \alpha \cos \alpha.$$

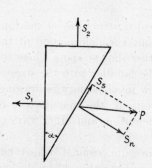

Fig. 1.—Stresses on the sides of an elementary prism, two sides being principal planes.

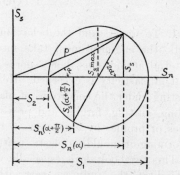

Fig. 2.—Mohr's stress circle

When we express these stresses in terms of the double angle 2α,

$$s_n = \frac{s_1 + s_2}{2} + \frac{s_1 - s_2}{2} \cos 2\alpha;$$

$$s_s = \frac{s_1 - s_2}{2} \sin 2\alpha.$$

Representing these results graphically by plotting s_n as abscissæ and s_s as ordinates (fig. 2), it may be shown that the points form a circle, *Mohr's stress circle*.

The distance from the point (s_n, s_s) to the origin gives the resultant stress p for the plane α. These formulæ and this mode of representation will be frequently used. Some properties of the stresses which must be constantly kept in mind are enumerated.

1. In two-dimensional problems of plasticity two perpendicular planes may be assigned at every point where no tangential stress occurs. On one of these planes the normal stress is a maximum and on the other it is a minimum.

2. The tangential or shear stresses on normal planes are equal and are directed either to or from the common line.

3. The maximum shear stresses occur on planes making angles of 45° with the principal planes.

4. The normal stress s_n as well as the total stress p, are equal for the planes of maximum shear stress.

5. When the normal stresses s_{n1}, s_{n2}, and the shear stress s_s are known for two perpendicular planes, the principal stresses are calculated from the formula

$$\frac{s_1}{s_2} = \frac{s_{n1} + s_{n2}}{2} \pm \sqrt{\left(\frac{s_{n1} - s_{n2}}{2}\right)^2 + s_s^2}.$$

6. The maximum shear stress is calculated from the formula

$$(s_s)_{max} = \pm \sqrt{\left(\frac{s_{n1} - s_{n2}}{2}\right)^2 + s_s^2}.$$

The attentive reader will have already thought of the influence on plastic flow of the third principal stress, acting in the direction of the axis of the prismatic solid which we are to consider deformed over its cross-sectional profile only. At first he would be inclined to believe that, like the axial strains, the axial stresses are everywhere zero, and when s_1 and s_2 have equal signs (which generally is the case) the greatest shear stress would occur in planes making angles of 45° with the axis. This would make plane problems complicated. We therefore now mention that in dealing with three-dimensional plastic flow, we shall prove that in the two-dimensional cases of plastic flow the axial stress adjusts itself either to the maximum or to the

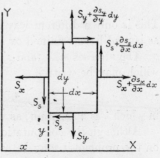

Fig. 3.—The differential stress-increases on the sides of an element are in equilibrium.

minimum principal stress. We can draw another stress circle for the axial stress and the axial principal stress. But this stress circle is identical with that under consideration, and displacements in directions for which it is drawn do not occur. Axial stress need not then be considered.

2. If we consider the equilibrium of an element of the material $dx\,dy$ with unit length in the direction normal to our plane (fig. 3),

and compute the forces acting in the directions X and Y, neglecting the weight of the element, we can write down the relations

$$\frac{\partial s_x}{\partial x} + \frac{\partial s_s}{\partial y} = 0,$$

$$\frac{\partial s_y}{\partial y} + \frac{\partial s_s}{\partial x} = 0.$$

The exact calculation of these stresses requires the solution of the differential equations. In general, there is an infinite number of solutions. We have to find that one which agrees with the imposed forces and complies internally with a condition which is different in the case of elastic and of plastic deformation. For plastic deformation in plane problems this condition can be expressed simply. But before proceeding to it, we must mention that instead of trying to find a solution of these equations which suits the external forces and fulfils the condition of plasticity for a simple case, we may attempt to guess the so-called *Airy's stress function*. This is a function F of x and y, so built up that the stresses are obtained from it by double differentiation:

$$s_x = \frac{\partial^2 F}{\partial y^2}, \quad s_y = \frac{\partial^2 F}{\partial x^2}, \quad s_s = -\frac{\partial^2 F}{\partial x \, \partial y}.$$

This is only a different way of expressing the equations of equilibrium as is readily ascertained by substitution.

The stresses s_x, s_y and s_s must also fulfil the *condition of plasticity* which may be written

$$(s_x - s_y)^2 + 4s_s{}^2 = 4k^2,$$

in which k is a constant, as will be explained in the next paragraph.

Although the computation of Airy's function throws no more light on the problem it may be useful as a kind of mathematical control.

3. *What is the test for plasticity?* This is a physical question. We confine ourselves to the principal engineering material, mild steel with 0·1 per cent carbon, normalized at about 900° C. so that it is as ductile as possible. All other malleable metals and, in general, all plastic materials, behave more or less similarly. Let us consider the elongation curve for a test bar (fig. 4). The elastic elongation ϵ_e may be neglected as it does not even amount to $\frac{1}{20}$ * of the plastic elongation

---

* Fritsche: " Die Tragfähigkeit von Balken aus Stahl mit Berücksichtigung des plastischen Verformungsvermögens ", *Der Bauingenieur*, 1930, p. 852.

ϵ_p. In considering the total extension the coefficient of elasticity may be taken as $E = \infty$.* Moreover, in the problems we have to solve, the elastic deformations are not considered.

Can we explain the fluctuations in the stress-strain diagram, drawn in ordinary and extended scale in fig. 4, after the upper yield limit has been attained? We shall say more about this in the last chapters, but here we give an incomplete explanation.

In cooling after annealing, innumerable ferrite crystals grow from nuclei differently orientated. The variation of some constants of the steel, such as resistance to shearing in different directions with respect

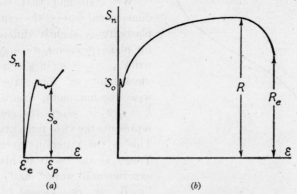

(a)   (b)

Fig. 4.—Stress-strain curve for a tensile test on mild steel, the stress s_n referred to the initial cross-section. In (b) the horizontal scale is increased to 7 times that in (a).

to the crystal axis, plays a part, but we think that the small jumps in the curve are principally due to the gradual breakdown of the brittle skeleton of either cementite or ferrous oxide of iron which binds the crystallites. The great ductility and small resistance to displacement of the atoms in the crystals ceases to hold after a certain elongation. By further deformation the metal becomes stronger. Fig. 5, in which stress is calculated for the actual contracted cross-section, shows to what degree iron can be strengthened by stretching.†

In our theory of plasticity we accept that considerable change of form occurs at constant stress. For red-hot iron, some modern plastics,

* F. Körber and A. Eischinger: "Formänderungswiderstand kaltgerechten Stahles". *Mitt K. Wilhelm Inst. Eisenforschung*, Bd. 26, Lfg. 3, fig. 450, Düsseldorf, 1943.
This is an experimental proof of the validity of our assumptions. It is also shown that the resistance to shearing in metals is not influenced by the normal stresses.

† P. Ludwik: "Die Bedeutung des Gleit- und Reiswiderstandes für die Werkstoffprüfung", *Zeitschr. der Ver. d. Ing.*, 1927, p. 1532.

and doughy or unguinous matter, this is a good basis for computation, and in the case of annealed mild steel it may be applied for moderate deformation. We thus build our theory of plasticity on the idealized stress-strain diagram represented by fig. 6. *The criterion for plasticity in two-dimensional problems can then be formulated by saying that during plastic flow the difference between the two principal stresses remains constant.* According to the stress circle (fig. 2) this difference is equal to the limit of elasticity or yield limit, and twice the maximum shearing stress, which we call tangential yield stress.

We shall find that for three-dimensional stress, the criterion of plasticity is slightly different, but for plane problems we may simply write $s_1 - s_2 = s_0$, in which s_0 is the yield limit, or, formulated otherwise, the maximum shearing stress $k = s_0/2$, in which the constant k represents the yield tangential stress. This is the criterion given by H. Tresca as the result of his famous experimental work * and accepted by B. de. St. Venant † for the mathematical solution of problems of plasticity. Neglecting the elastic strain ϵ_e we only use the horizontal part of fig. 6. A clearer condition of plasticity is inconceivable.

Fig. 5.—Stress-strain curve for a tensile test on mild steel, the stress s_n referred to the actual cross-section.

The simplest problem of plasticity is shown in fig. 7. The plastic material is compressed between perfectly lubricated parallel planes. One must appreciate, that at any point $s_x = 0$, $s_y = s_0$, $s_s = 0$ ($s_0 =$ yield stress), the condition of plasticity is satisfied and that Airy's function is

$$F = s_0 \frac{x^2}{2}.$$

During plastic flow the volume is constant. Each element becomes shorter in the direction of the smallest principal stress (when pressure is called negative stress) and longer in the direction of the greatest principal stress. In fig. 7 lines of maximum shearing stress are indi-

* "Mémoires sur l'écoulement des corps solides", *Mémoires de l'Académie des Sciences*, XX, 1872, p. 281.

† *Comptes rendues*, 1870–1.

cated. Often these lines are confused with slip lines. The inclination of
these lines comes within 10° of that of the lines or planes which sometimes appear on the surface of cold-drawn mild steel, and may be
observed as dull lines on a polished surface, or as flaws in the scale or
in specially brittle lacquers or varnishes covering the metal. These
lines, however, are due to a sudden drop from upper to lower yielding
stress and are distinct from the theoretical lines of maximum shearing
stress. We shall devote a special chapter (XVIII) to their meaning.

It will be of little use going on with the study of this manual if the
reader has no opportunity of making some simple tests on plastic
materials. By etching (after heat treatment) of polished sections of

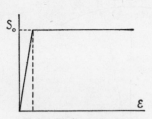

Fig. 6.—Idealized stress-strain
curve for plastic material. The
horizontal line replaces the curve
of the former diagrams.

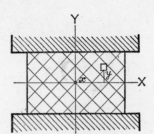

Fig. 7.—Plastic mass com-
pressed between perfectly lubricated parallel planes. The
trajectories of maximum shear
stress are drawn.

cold-strained mild steel test pieces with Fry's liquid (a solution of
copper chloride and ammonium chloride) the regions of plastic flow
become visible.

In the crystal lattice the iron atoms are bound by atomic forces.
Much smaller cohesive forces have to be overcome for an internal
change in the ranks of atoms in the crystallites than for their separation. Indeed, in our study of theoretical plasticity, we consider the
cohesive forces as invincible and only take into account the shear
stresses. As soon as these attain their critical value the particles leave
their former ranks and take up new positions. All the energy accumu-
lated to overcome the atomic forces of cohesion is available as energy
of oscillation when the atom has jumped to its new position and is
dissipated as heat.

4. It has become a practice to calculate the dimensions of steel
beams according to the theory of plasticity, and there is usually no
objection to this custom.

If we adhere to Navier's hypothesis and assume that plane sections normal to the neutral axis remain plane after bending (which is generally accepted), the bending stress in all parts of the section where the yield strain is exceeded will be $s_n = s_0$. The distribution of the stress as a function of the distance to the neutral layer may be represented by a broken line identical to the stress-strain line of the tensile test (fig. 8). If we call the width of an element of the section b, and z the distance to

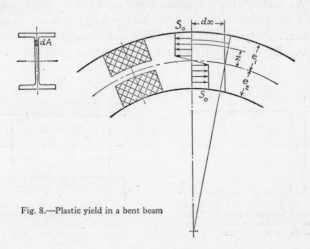

Fig. 8.—Plastic yield in a bent beam

the neutral line, the equilibrium of the moment of normal stresses and the bending moment gives, as the yield limit is attained on the whole section,

$$M = s_0 \int_0^{e_1} bz\,dz + s_0 \int_{-e_2}^0 bz\,dz = s_0(S_1 + S_2),$$

where S_1 and S_2 represent the static moments of the parts of the section above and below the neutral line, whose thicknesses are e_1 and e_2 respectively. This is the bending moment which the beam withstands, without taking into account any reinforcement by cold-bending. By adopting a factor of safety, the beam is actually loaded to a fraction of the critical bending moment.

Formerly beams were computed by the formula $M = s_0 \dfrac{I}{e}$, in which I represents the moment of inertia of the section for the neutral line, and a safety factor was taken for the stress in the outer fibres. For the rectangular section the difference between $\dfrac{I}{e} = \dfrac{bh^2}{6}$ and $S_1 + S_2 = \dfrac{bh^2}{4}$

is 50 per cent. For rolled I-beams the difference is at the most 16 per cent, and for a reason to be mentioned in Chap. XXI, the former method of computation was too safe.*

In fig. 8 we have also drawn the lines of maximum shearing stress, which make angles of 45° with the direction in which the fibres are stressed.

The application of this part of the theory of plasticity has become a special branch in the calculation of steel structures. We shall not treat it in this book. The reader is referred to other sources.†

---

* To understand the validity of this method of calculation of beams, see L'Hermite, *L'Expérience et les Théories Nouvelles en Résistance des Matériaux*, p. 97, &c. (Flexion).

† Fritsche: "Arbeitsgesetze bei elastischer Balkenbiegung", *Zeitschr. f. Angew, Math. und. Mech.*, 1931–2.

Kist: "La deformation en palier de l'acier substitué à la loi de Hooke comme base de calcul de la résistance des ponts et charpentes métalliques", *L'Oss. Métallique*, 1933, pp. 176–88.

F. Bleich: "La ductibilité de l'acier, son application au dimensionnement des systèmes hyperstatiques", *L'oss. Métallique*, 1934.

Colonnetti: "Les deformations plastiques et le dimensionnement des systèmes hyperstatiques", *L'Oss. Metall.*, 7 (1938), 331–5, 483–8; 8 (1939), 147–50.

Maier-Leibniz: "Versuche zur weiteren Klärung der Frage der tatsächlichen Tragfähigkeit durchlaufender Träger aus Baustahl", *Stahlbau* (1939), pp. 153–60.

Swift: "Plastic flow in metals; a survey of the present position", *The Metal Industry*, Vol. LVI (1940), pp. 127–30, 149–52, 173–5.

CHAPTER II

The Thick-walled Cylinder

1. A good example of a problem in plasticity is the computation of the strength of thick hollow cylinders under internal pressure. The solution has been known for more than thirty years.*

The equilibrium of the wall between the radii a and r indicated in fig. 9 is expressed by

$$pa - s_r r + \int_a^r s_t \, dr = 0,$$

and after differentiation

$$s_t - s_r = r \frac{\partial s_r}{\partial r}.$$

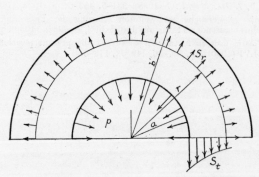

Fig. 9.—Stress equilibrium in the wall of a cylinder

For reasons of symmetry, the radial and tangential stresses are principal stresses, and their difference is $2k = s_0$, in which k is the critical shearing stress and s_0 the yield stress.

$$\therefore \ r \frac{\partial s_r}{\partial r} = 2k$$

and

$$s_r = 2k \log_e r + C.$$

---

* F. van Iterson: "The strength of thick hollow cylinders", *Engineering*, 5th Jan., 1912, p. 22.

C. A. Smith: *Engineering*, 5th March, 1909, p. 327, was very near the same solution.

When there is no tension at the outer surface of the cylinder and the wall is plastified throughout, the constant C may be determined and the stresses in the wall at r are

$$s_r = 2k \log_e \frac{r}{b}.$$

The internal pressure which makes the wall flow throughout its thickness is

$$p = -2k \log_e \frac{b}{a}.$$

We must make an important comment on the behaviour of mild-steel cylinders. When the pressure is increased to the point where the yield limit is exceeded throughout the whole wall, the cylinder expands and the steel becomes stronger. Along the line where the cylinder will burst, the wall contracts, and if the ratio b/a is not too great the wall behaves like a tensile bar of the same material. It may be expected that the formula will hold right up to the bursting pressure

$$p = R \log_e \frac{b}{a},$$

in which R is the tensile strength of the steel.

The question as to whether determinations of strength based on the condition of plasticity are confirmed by experiment is so important that a table of the results of very careful tests is inserted here.*

BURSTING PRESSURE OF THICK CYLINDERS

Ratio of external to internal radius b/a	Bursting pressure p in kg./cm.^{2}	Tensile strength of the steel calculated from formula $R = p \div \log_e \frac{b}{a}$ in kg./cm.^{2}	Tensile strength of the steel obtained from ordinary test bars. R in kg./cm.^{2}
1·35	1187	3950	3820
1·53	1628	3830	3820
1·58	1745	3825	3820
1·67	1910	3725	4140
1·67	1920	3750	4140
1·71	2120	3950	4140
1·77	2165	3790	3820
1·79	2140	3680	3820
1·79	2280	3920	3820
Average	—	3820	3936

* Cook and Robertson: " The strength of thick hollow cylinders under internal pressure ", *Engineering*, 15th Dec., 1911, p. 786.

When calculating the dimensions of cylinders with this formula we may employ the same factor of safety as is used in applying the theory of elasticity.

In polar co-ordinates the stresses derived from Airy's stress function $F(r, \phi)$ are

$$s_r = \frac{1}{r^2}\frac{\partial^2 F}{\partial \phi^2} + \frac{1}{r}\frac{\partial F}{\partial r},$$

$$s_t = \frac{\partial^2 F}{\partial r^2},$$

$$s_s = -\frac{\partial}{\partial r}\left(\frac{1}{r}\frac{\partial F}{\partial \phi}\right).$$

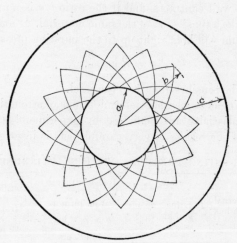

Fig. 10.—Maximum shear-stress trajectories in a partly plastified cylinder wall

In our case, as the stresses only depend on r, the stress function is

$$F(r) = 2k\left(\frac{r^2}{2}\log_e \frac{r}{b} - \frac{r^2}{4}\right).$$

When the pressure in the cylinder is gradually increased the steel gives way at the inner side when

$$p = -\frac{c^2 - a^2}{c^2} \times k = -\frac{c^2 - a^2}{2c^2} \times s_0.$$

Here a and c are the inner and outer radii of the cylinder (fig. 10).

The negative sign indicates that we are dealing with pressure. We can calculate for a given pressure the circle limiting the plastified and elastically strained regions in the wall. To understand the last and the following formula we must combine the stress calculation according to the theory of elasticity given by Lamé with that according to the theory of plasticity. The elastic limit lies where the difference between the two principal stresses as given by Lamé's theory is

$$s_t - s_r = 2k = s_0,$$

in which s_0 is the yield limit found by a tensile test. When the pressure is increased, the plastic region extends. It reaches the radius b when

$$p = -2k \log_e \frac{b}{a} - k \frac{c^2 - b^2}{c^2}.$$

The trajectories giving the directions of the principal stresses form a network of radii and circles. The trajectories for the maximum shear stresses form a network of logarithmic spirals crossing the trajectories of principal stress at angles of 45°, and this is true both in the region of elastic deformation and in the region of plastic deformation. These lines have the peculiarity that the shearing stress is constant along a trajectory and attains the value $s_s = k$, the yield shear stress. We shall see that in the plastic region these lines are of special significance and therefore are drawn in our figure.

But to avoid misunderstanding we emphasize that these trajectories, here logarithmic spirals, must not be confounded with slip lines. The material of the wall is extended tangentially, and compressed radially. When the wall is stretched the constituent particles change neighbours, and take up new positions. In plastic flow there is no question of slip lines or slip planes.

2. The technical applications of plastic flow in cylinder walls are numerous. We mention the construction of guns by shrinking tubes on each other; the assembling of engine parts such as crankshafts; the fixing of rail wagon wheels on their axles, drilled $\frac{1}{1000}$ of the diameter too small, either by pressure or shrinking. An interesting instance is the sinking of mine shafts by congelation of the soil, on which subject many experiments have been made and much has been written.*

* Les Cuvelages, par Lucien Denoël (Paris, 1915), p. 165, &c., "Le procédé de fonçage par congélation".

In fig. 11 we give a photograph of a cylinder of annealed mild steel, burst by internal pressure. This figure really belongs to a subsequent chapter, but may also serve as an illustration here. The ends of the tube are reinforced. We may assume that in the thinner part flat sections remain flat after plastification. This certainly is true for the middle section.

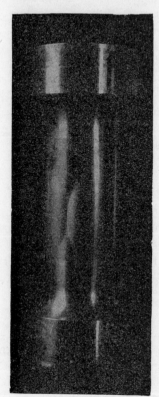

Fig. 11.—Ruptured thick-walled cylinder (bore of square section)

The question arises whether it makes a difference in the bursting pressure if the flanges are kept at a constant distance apart, whether the oil pressure is exerted by a well-fitting plunger so that the mean axial tension is zero, or whether the oil enters through a side hole in the flanges in such a way that the wall is submitted to axial tension. We must defer the examination of these problems until the criterion of three-dimensional plasticity is treated. Here we can only assert that it makes no difference to the bursting pressure. The axial tension is either equal to the greatest or to the smallest principal stress, $s_z = s_t$ or $s_z = s_r$ and is distributed in such a way that the axial force is kept in equilibrium by the axial tensions. It will be difficult for the reader to believe that in a closed cylinder the axial tension at a certain radius jumps from pressure to tension. Such things only happen in plastified regions and it is hard to depart from conceptions ingrained by the study of elasticity.

CHAPTER III

The Theorem of Hencky and the Plastic Sector

1. The solution of plane or two-dimensional problems of plasticity is often facilitated by the application of Hencky's theorem, which may be formulated:

Proceeding along a trajectory of yield shearing stress, both principal stresses s_1 and s_2, and the normal stress s_n increase with $2k\phi$, where $k =$ yield shearing stress and ϕ the angle in radians through which the tangent and the normal to the trajectory have turned.

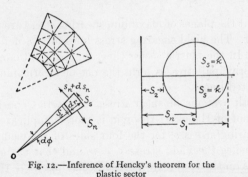

Fig. 12.—Inference of Hencky's theorem for the plastic sector

Before proving this theorem in the general case we shall take it for the plastic sector. In the problems of plasticity with which the engineer has to deal in his daily practice, the plastic sector so often plays the essential part that the next chapter will be devoted wholly to its applications.

Keeping in mind that in many instances a plastic sector occurs, it is often possible to guess the shear-stress trajectories. The next thing to do is to calculate the stresses along the contours of the plastic region and to test if these can be brought into agreement with the pressure exerted on the free surface. The problems in the next chapter are all treated in this way.

A part of the plastic sector is shown in fig. 12. The radii and circles are lines of maximum or yield shearing stress $s_s = k$. It is easy to give in polar co-ordinates the normal stress s_n, and the principal stresses s_1 and s_2 satisfying the conditions of internal equilibrium. The element $r d\phi dr$ indicated in the figure must be in equilibrium. We take the moments of the stresses acting on the sides about the centre of the sector:

$$\frac{\partial(s_s r^2 d\phi)}{\partial r} dr = \frac{\partial s_n}{\partial \phi} d\phi r dr.$$

Thus

$$\frac{\partial s_n}{\partial \phi} = 2 s_s = 2k,$$

and

$$s_n = C + 2k\phi,$$

which proves the theorem.

The stress circle shows

$$s_1 = s_n + k = C + 2k\phi + k,$$
$$s_2 = s_n - k = C + 2k\phi - k,$$
$$s_1 - s_2 = 2k = s_0.$$

It is clear that the planes of maximum shearing stress are perpendicular to each other. The yield shearing-stress lines form a net of orthogonal trajectories. In the plastic sector they are radii and circles. The trajectories of principal stresses form the net of logarithmic spirals indicated by dotted lines.

When both systems of shear-stress trajectories consist of curved lines, the proof of Hencky's theorem is more complicated. We know that the shearing stress s_s for the four sides of the element indicated in fig. 13 reaches the yield stress $s_s = k$, and that the accompanying normal stress on the conjugate perpendicular planes is the same. The components of the forces on the sides acting in the direction of r_1 balance, hence

$$\frac{\partial}{\partial r_1} (s_n r_1 d\phi) dr_1 - s_s dr_2 d\psi - s_n r_2 d\psi d\phi - s_s r_1 d\phi d\psi = 0,$$

and $\therefore s_s(r_1 d\phi d\psi + dr_2 d\psi) = s_n(dr_1 d\phi - r_2 d\psi d\phi) + \dfrac{\partial s_n}{\partial r_1} r_1 d\phi dr_1.$

The figure shows $r_2 d\psi = dr_1$ and $dr_2 = r_1 d\phi.$

Therefore

$$2 s_s r_1 d\phi d\psi = \frac{\partial s_n}{\partial r_1} r_1 d\phi dr_1$$

or

$$ds_n = 2k d\psi,$$

$$\therefore s_n = C_1 + 2k\psi.$$

In the same way we find

$$s_n = C_2 + 2k\phi.$$

Let us apply Hencky's theorem to calculate the stresses in the wall of the thick cylinder, assuming that the logarithmic spirals at 45° to the radii and circles are the shearing-stress trajectories. They are given by

$$r = ae^{\varphi} \text{ or } \phi = \log_e \frac{r}{a}.$$

Hencky's theorem prescribes for the point r

$$s_n = C + 2k\phi,$$

hence
$$s_n = C + 2k \log_e \frac{r}{a}.$$

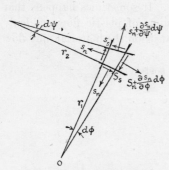

Fig. 13.—The equilibrium of an element enclosed between four trajectories of maximum shear stress illustrates the theory of Hencky.

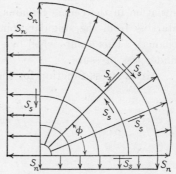

Fig. 14.—The paradox of the plastic sector

The solution of our problem then is

$$s_t = C + 2k \log_e \frac{r}{a} + k,$$

$$s_r = C + 2k \log_e \frac{r}{a} - k,$$

$$s_t - s_r = 2k.$$

2. Often the engineer has to deal with plane problems in which the plastic sector extends right up to the centre, and he is then confronted with an absurdity.

In fig. 14 we have indicated that along the trajectories, radii and circles, the shear stress invariably is $s_s = k$; that the corresponding normal stress s_n remains constant along each radius but increases with $2k$ when we proceed along a circle. But near the centre we encounter first the absurdity, that on one of two perpendicular planes, the shearing stress s_s is directed both towards and away from the line of intersection. (See Chap. I, § 1, 1 and 2.) Next we are puzzled by the absurdity that, although s_n as shown by the stress circle must be equal on the two sides, here the difference of s_n on these two planes amounts to $2k\phi$.

We often find such paradoxes at singular points where the solution no longer holds. The difficulty is overcome by imagining a small cylinder with a perfectly rough surface at the centre, as indicated in fig. 14. When it is clear that then any paradox has disappeared, we may let the edge shrink to less than a hair's thickness. But still the situation in the centre remains unstable. It sometimes happens that starting from the singular point the regime of plastic flow suddenly changes. This occurs when by such a transition the material may flow under less pressure.

Airy's stress function for the plastic sector is

$$F = kr^2\phi + C\,\frac{r^2}{2}.$$

CHAPTER IV

The Solution of Plasticity Problems by means of the Plastic Sector

1. In general, problems on plasticity are easier to solve than the corresponding problems on elasticity and they are different in this respect, that the stress trajectories need not be continuous. Several patterns or networks of shear stress trajectories may be fitted together, provided that along the boundaries of the different patterns the tangents to the lines coincide.

As networks of trajectories in different regions the simplest solutions, e.g. straight lines, radii and circles, logarithmic spirals and cycloids, have to be tried first. The different patterns must join like the pieces of a jigsaw puzzle. This difference compared with stress trajectories in problems of elasticity results from the fact that the condition of plasticity only prescribes that along the trajectories $s_s = k$. No continuity in deformation is needed. Plasticity gives much freedom in displacement, as we shall see when dealing with three-dimensional stress. For the solution of plane stress problems the equations of internal equilibrium and the condition of plasticity are adequate.

We start with the classical problem solved by Prandtl * from which the theory of plasticity has been evolved.

The resistance to yielding under a pressure p exerted on the blunt edge of the wedge of indefinite length represented in fig. 15 is to be determined. The plastified part of the section, when the critical pressure p has been reached, may be divided into five regions. One isosceles triangle ABC under the loaded portion, which is pressed downward into the plastic mass, two similar triangles ADE pressed out of flanks connected to the middle region by two plastic sectors ACD.

The reader must be well aware that wherever a flat surface is evenly loaded until there is subsidence of the underlying material, a plastic region of right-angled triangular section originates. This is the only figure which may be filled by orthogonal trajectories inclined at 45°

---

* " Ueber die Eindringungsfestigkeit (Härte) plastischer Baustoffe und die Festigkeit von Scheiben ", *Zeitschr. angew. Mech.*, 1921, p. 15.

to the direction of loading. It also holds true for the unloaded flanks.

The lines of demarcation AC, BC, AD and DE are also lines of yield shearing stress. Within the right-angled triangles, in the regions filled with straight lines, the stresses are the same at all the points, as is the case in fig. 7, which indeed may be developed from fig. 15 by taking the plastic sectors $\alpha = 0$. Only in the plastic sectors do the stresses increase. Along the flanks AE they are $s_1 = 2k$ and $s_2 = 0$ at the moment of plastic yielding. This time we omit the negative sign, as we are dealing with pressure.

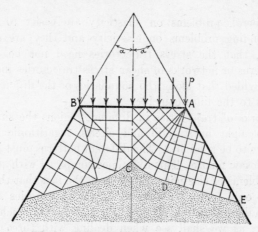

Fig. 15.—Yield pressure on the upper side of a blunt wedge: at the right maximum shear-stress trajectories, at the left principal stress trajectories.

By drawing the stress circle for the points of ADE, it is clear that along the line AD we have the normal stress $s_n = k$ and the shearing stress $s_s = k$. In the plastic sectors s_n increases and reaches

$$s_n = k + 2k\alpha$$

along the line AC. On the upper surface we get the pressure

$$p = s_1 = 2k(1 + \alpha),$$

and the other principal stress in the region ABC is

$$s_2 = 2k\alpha.$$

We repeat, the resistance to plastic flow of the blunt wedge with angle 2α is

$$p = 2k(1 + \alpha) = s_0(1 + \alpha).$$

Mild steel is made stronger by cold deformation. Supposing that the theory of plasticity holds true up to breakdown, then the ultimate resistance is

$$p = R(1 + \alpha),$$

where R is the resistance to compression. This decreases to $p = R$ in the case represented in fig. 7.

2. When the angle of the plastic sector becomes $\alpha = \pi/2$, we have to deal with the problem of the loaded strip on the flat surface of a plastic body, for instance, a plate of lead or mild steel of sufficient thickness (at least $\sqrt{2}a$, if a is half the width of the loaded strip).

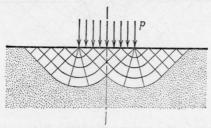

Fig. 16.—Penetration of a triangular prism under constant pressure along a strip of the surface of plastic material

The maximum load to be applied to a strip on the surface of a plastic body is, as may be calculated with the formula given in § 1, for fig. 16,

$$p = (1 + \pi/2)2k = (1 + \pi/2)s_0, \text{ where } s_0 = \text{yielding stress},$$

or
$$p = (1 + \pi/2)R$$

if the strengthening by cold-working is taken into account.

The applicability of the formula has been proved experimentally by A. Nadai.* But the examination of the extent of the plastic region by Fry's method has shown an apparent inconsistency.

Before the plastic matter bulges on the surface at both sides of the loaded strip the triangular wedge is pushed down into the underlying layers which give way partly by elastic and partly by plastic deformation, until they offer a resistance

$$p = 2 \cdot 57 s_0.$$

* " Versuche über die plastischen Formänderungen von keilförmigen Körpern aus Flusseisen ", A. Nadai, *Zeitschr. für angewandte Mathematik und Mechanik*, 1921, p. 15.

A region with rootlike spurs is visible on the etched section, but these supplementary plastified streaks do not affect the ultimate resistance to plastic flow. The outer lines of demarcation at 45° agree exactly with the boundaries indicated in fig. 16.

3. The appearance of the plastic sector will often suffice to give an insight into the shape and extent of the regions of plastic deformation, but some practice is needed in plotting the isosceles right-angled triangles and the plastic sectors. We shall give some examples.

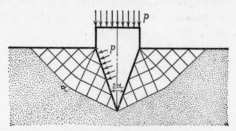

Fig. 17.—Plastic flow at the sides of a perfectly
lubricated knife-blade

Fig. 17 represents the regions of plastic flow at both sides of the indentation made by a perfectly lubricated knife-blade. The pattern can be completed by analogy with fig. 16 and the pressure at yielding must be

$$p = 2k(1 + \alpha) = s_0(1 + \alpha).$$

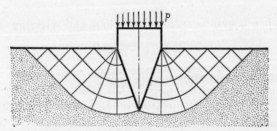

Fig. 18.—Plastic flow at the sides of a knife-blade whose
surfaces are as rough as those of a file

If, as shown in fig. 18, the wedge surfaces are perfectly rough, so that we have to deal with yield shearing stresses, then $k = s_0/2$ along the surfaces and the angle of the plastic sector becomes 45° + α. The pressure needed to push the knife into the plastic mass amounts to

$$p = k(1 + \pi/2 + 2\alpha + \cot \alpha).$$

4. The processes of cutting metal, turning, planing, milling, drilling, acquire a physical basis by application of the plastic sector. In fig. 19 the plastic region is indicated for the edge of a block of iron uniformly loaded to the yield point. Perhaps it might be expected that the edge would be pushed off as a whole at an angle of 45°, but a glance at fig. 4 makes it clear that the strengthening of the steel causes the plastification of the entire edge.

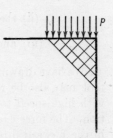

As an exercise the student may draw the trajectories for maximum shear in the case where the corner angle is larger or smaller than 90°. The latter case needs practice with bent bars of decreasing section as shown in fig. 8.* For the case represented in fig. 19 the pressure needed to remove the metal is

Fig. 19.—Edge of a block of metal uniformly loaded until yield occurs. The maximum shear-stress trajectories are drawn.

$$p = 2s_s = R,$$

where s_s is the shearing strength and R the hypothetical crushing strength.

The simplest representation of metal-cutting is obtained by

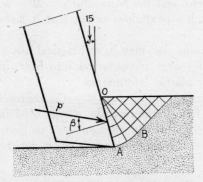
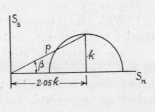

Fig. 20.—Metal-cutting with tool friction.   The stress circle and resultant pressure are indicated for the surface of the tool

imagining the pressure p to be exerted by a perfectly lubricated tool. The chips then creep along the front surface of the tool. But an instance in better agreement with practice is shown in fig. 20 for a cutting edge of 15° and sufficient friction between chip and tool.   The angle AOB

---

* As this problem may be too difficult for some readers we give the solution in § 8 of the penultimate chapter.

of the plastic section as shown in the figure is 30°. On the pushing plane of the tool act

(i) the tangential stress $s_s = k$,

(ii) the normal stress $s_n = k(1 + 2 \cdot \pi/6) = 2 \cdot 05k$.

(iii) and the principal stress $s_1 = 3 \cdot 05k$.

We have drawn the stress circle, so that the resultant stress p on the tool may also be read in the figure. It will be clear that by roughing with high-speed tools the angle β remains less than the angle of friction. The force exerted by the tool may be resolved into a component in the forward direction and another in the direction of the feed. If we calculate these components with $2k = R$, the tensile strength, we find no agreement with test results; but if we take into account that, at the blue tempering-colour of the chips, the resistance is 30 per cent higher than at normal temperature, and that work-hardening to which the steel is subjected further raises the resistance, we may be very satisfied with the agreement.* In fact, computing backwards, we find $R = 75$ kg./mm.² for steel of a tensile strength of 37–40 kg./mm.²

Once more we look at the isosceles right-angled triangle of fig. 20. The vertical principal stress is zero, and the horizontal $s = 2k = R$. The material is compressed to such a prodigious extent that it flows along the tool.

The theory suggests some remarks that may be of practical use.

1. With blunt tools frictional energy is converted into heat, in addition to the energy needed for plastic deformation.

2. The resistance of steel is a maximum at about 220° C. By cooling and lubricating the working face of the tool, the energy used in cutting metals is somewhat reduced. If the lubrication could be made perfect an appreciable decrease in energy consumption might be attained.

---

* Werkstoffbücher 61 K. Krekeler: Die Zerspanbarkeit der Werkstoffe; see graph, p. 15.

We see that the forward component is $H = 2700$ kg. for a chip of 30 mm.² section. This gives a pressure component of 90 kg./mm.² Our fig. 20 shows that this pressure is $2 \cdot 4 k$. Hence $R = 2k = 75$ kg./mm.² for mild steel of 37–40 kg./mm.² tensile strength. But according to Herbert and Kronenberg, *Die Härte der Werkstoffe Maschinenbau*, 1927, p. 993, fig. 6, who measured the increase of hardness near the edge of the tool by the Brinell test, we see that by work-hardening the hardness increases 70 per cent and even more at blue colour.

Compare fig. 74, " Die Scherspanbildung im Eisen ", *Verein deustcher Ingenieure Forschungsheft*, 350 (1931).

" Grundlagen der Zerspanung von Krystof und Schalbroch ", *Berichte über betriebwissenschaftlichen Arbeiten*, Bd. 12, 1939.

3. If the cutting angle θ, which we took as 15°, is taken larger, the force and energy for cutting steel decreases, but we only recommend this practice for soft materials.

4. At the same cutting angle, coefficient of friction and temperature, the energy consumption per cm.^{3} of chips will be the same for turning, drilling and milling. But if cooling and lubricating are best in milling, then this method of cutting metals has some advantages.

The energy consumed in the deformation of plastic materials is converted into heat. The first determination of the mechanical equivalent of heat was made by Count Rumford in the eighteenth century in a test on drilling guns,* and not long ago Professor N. N. Saurin of the Skoda Works carried out a similar experiment on turning steel.†

* *Phil. Transactions*, Vol. XVIII, p. 283.
† *Machinery*, Vol. 53, 23rd March, 1939, p. 802.

CHAPTER V

Plastic Deformation at Sharp Grooves

In a subsequent chapter we shall deal with cylindrical test pieces provided with a circumferential groove. This chapter is confined to two-dimensional problems. By this we do not mean notched strips or bars. If these are submitted to a tensile test, constriction soon becomes visible near the notches.*

Plane problems in the theory of plasticity contrast with those in the theory of elasticity in this respect, that it is essential that any deformation in the third dimension be prevented. For instance, the strips under examination must be grooved on the broad side.

1. We now consider a cylinder with a square boring, submitted to internal pressure. The calculation of the stresses according to the theory of elasticity reveals excessive stresses near the sharp corners, but the ductility of the steel prevents any extreme increase of stresses.

It has been accepted generally that the stresses are confined to the tensile yield limit. We shall see that this limit may be far surpassed.

For solving the problem of plasticity with the notation indicated in fig. 21 at the right, we have to find the solution of two simultaneous partial differential equations

$$\frac{\partial s_x}{\partial x} + \frac{\partial s_s}{\partial y} = 0, \quad \frac{\partial s_y}{\partial y} + \frac{\partial s_s}{\partial x} = 0,$$

which fulfil the condition of plasticity,

$$\left(\frac{s_x - s_y}{2}\right)^2 + s_s^2 = k^2,$$

in which k stands for the yield shear stress. In polar co-ordinates the equations are (fig. 21 at the left),

$$r \frac{\partial s_r}{\partial r} + \frac{\partial s_s}{\partial \phi} + (s_r - s_t) = 0,$$

---

* See the fine photograph (fig. 12), "Auftreten der ersten Fliesslinien bei Flachstäben mit Spitzkerben", *Thum und Wunderlich, Forschung*, Vol. 3 (1932), p. 267.

$$\frac{\partial s_t}{\partial \phi} + r \frac{\partial s_s}{\partial r} + 2s_s = 0,$$

$$\left(\frac{s_r - s_t}{2}\right)^2 + s_s^2 = k^2.$$

For an infinitely long cylinder we have to accept that the stresses along any radius remain constant and are a function of ϕ only. It is a difficult task to find a simple continuous distribution of stress for the whole region round the corner, resisting the pressure on the sides and providing constant normal stress in the line of symmetry. But as soon as the condition of continuity is given up and it is accepted that

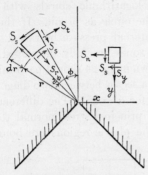

Fig. 21.—Stresses near the re-entrant angle in plastic material.

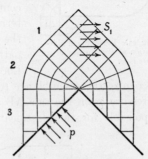

Fig. 22.—Maximum shear-stress trajectories near the corners of a hole with square section.

the plastic region may be divided into contiguous zones, the problem is easily solved, not only for the square hole but for any re-entrant corner.

Just as in the last chapter, we look for a plastic sector and immediately find the shear-stress lines drawn in fig. 22. We note three zones. In 1 and 3 the stresses are the same at all points. In 2 they remain constant along a radius and the principal and normal stresses increase proportionally with ϕ.

In the line of symmetry the main principal stress is

$$s_1 = 2k(1 + \pi/4) - p$$

when the internal pressure is p, and

$$s_1 = \pm \, 2k(1 + \pi/4)$$

when the body (of any shape) with a square boring is compressed or drawn at the periphery.

The main stress in the plastified region in this case is independent of the forces on the surface and amounts to

$$s_1 = 1.785s_0,$$

which is $78\frac{1}{2}$ per cent more than the yield stress s_0.

When a structure with a square hole is lightly loaded, plastic flow occurs in minute regions near the corners. These regions extend as the load is increased.

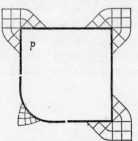

At the left bottom corner of fig. 23 we have shown the shear-stress lines for a rounded corner. These trajectories are orthogonal logarithmic spirals with the centre of the circle as origin. If the external or internal pressure be raised until the plastic zones are fully developed, the pattern shown in fig. 24 should be obtained.

Fig. 23.—Beginning of plastification at the corners of a square hole.

Looking at a sector between two diagonals, we recognize the resemblance to fig. 15 for $\alpha = 45°$. The difference in the pressure p on the side AB and the principal stress normal to AE is responsible for the plastification. The plastic regions are bounded

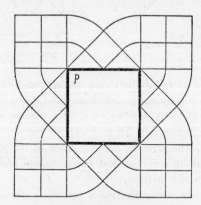

Fig. 24.—Fully developed plastic regions around a square hole

by the line CDE. Beyond these, incalculable elastic deformations occur, due to the known pressures exerted along these lines.

An extension of the problem requiring some advanced knowledge is given in Chap. XXIII, 4.

2. We must now calculate the bursting pressure for a thick-walled cylinder with a square hole (fig. 25).

If the stress distribution which we have just computed holds up to the end, i.e. if

$$s_1 = 1 \cdot 785 s_0 - p,$$

a cylinder with a square boring would withstand a much higher pressure than a cylinder with a round boring with the same smallest wall

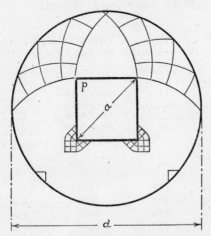

Fig. 25.—Regions of plastification in the wall of a thick cylinder with a boring of square section

Above: shear-stress trajectories leading to rupture.
Below: beginning of plastification.

thickness. (Note the final remark of Chap. III.) Plastic regions as indicated at the lower side of the figure start as soon as some pressure is put on the test cylinder. (They may be made visible by sawing the cylinder, polishing and etching the section.) But as the pressure becomes greater there comes a time when another solution of the plasticity-problem makes the metal yield to smaller pressures. Nature chooses this solution. It is the solution indicated in the upper half of the figure, that of the logarithmic spirals, starting from the outer wall with the centre as their origin, which at length prevails. With the notation of fig. 25, cylinder diameter d, diagonal of the boring a, the bursting pressure will be

$$p_e = 2k \log_e \frac{d}{a} = R \log_e \frac{d}{a},$$

in which k is the radius of the stress circle, the maximum shear stress after work-hardening, and R the tensile strength.

In this way we find the same formula for the ultimate strength as with the cylinder with a round hole and the same least wall thickness. Some tests were made, in order to test this formula.* The agreement was not so good as found for the cylinders with a cylindrical boring for which the test results are given in the table in Chap. II (p. 11).

Here are the results of our tests made with very homogeneous mild steel of $R = 40$ kg./mm.² tensile strength.

RESULTS OF TESTS ON THICK-WALLED CYLINDERS
WITH A BORING OF SQUARE SECTION

External diameter d, diagonal of square hole a and their ratio (mm.)			Bursting pressure p_e in kg. per sq. cm.	Bursting pressure p calculated from the formula $p = R \log_e \dfrac{d}{a}$	Ratio of the pressure found by test and by computation p_e/p	Tensile strength of the steel calculated from the formula $R = p_e/\log_e \dfrac{d}{a}$ in kg./mm.²
d	a	$\dfrac{d}{a}$				
20	14	1·43	1450	1440	1	40
40	14	2·86	4700	4200	1·12	45
55	14	3·93	7900	5473	1·44	57·5
70	14	5	8750	6438	1·25	50

Fig. 11 is a photograph of the cylinder with 55 mm. outer diameter.

The divergence between theory and experiment is instructive and must be discussed.

1. In Chap. II, § 1, we have already mentioned that the wall behaves like a test bar provided the ratio b/a is not too large. The tests of Cook and Robertson gave perfect agreement with theory because they have not exceeded the value 1·79. Prof. Michels of the High Pressure Laboratory at Amsterdam repeated these tests and found that with a larger value of b/a the bursting pressure rose above that given by the formula. For the same values of d/a as were investigated by Cook and Robertson, the agreement of experiment with theory was perfect.

2. The disagreement between formula and experiment for b/a and

* We are much indebted to Ir. Tummers of the Central Research Station of the State Mines and to Prof. Michels of the Van der Waals' Laboratories at Amsterdam for their assistance in making these difficult tests.

$d/a > 1\cdot79$ is due to prevention of contraction.   Although even at
small ratio values the contraction is somewhat less than for test bars,
cylinders with a not very thick wall bulge considerably before they
burst. The pressure then acts on a larger diameter which has a com-
pensating effect.

3. An elementary square in the plastic mass orientated according
to the principal stresses with sides a extends Δa in the direction of
the largest stress and becomes Δa shorter in the direction of the
smallest stress. We call

$$\sigma = \frac{2\,\Delta a}{a}$$

the *specific deformation*. If we investigate the value of the specific
deformation near the centre of the plastic sector, excessive values for

σ are found, which iron at normal
temperature cannot stand. The wall
is torn in a corner, and the thicker
the wall the sooner does the tear
occur. The oil pressure then acts in
the cleft, and this explains why at the
greater value of d/a, as given by the
last line of the table, the bursting
pressure again drops to the value given
by the formula.

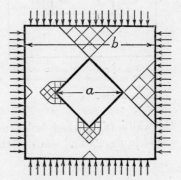

Fig. 26.—Regions of plastic flow
in the wall of a tube of square section
with square boring placed as in the
figure.

Below: initial plastification.
Above: ultimate plastification.

3. In the lower half of fig. 26 we
have drawn the beginning of plastic
flow for a tube of square section whose
square boring is placed athwart, and
in the upper half we have indicated
the flow-region which soon predomi-
nates and is maintained until rupture occurs. The bursting pressure
is calculated from the formula

$$p_e = \frac{b-a}{a}\,R,$$

because in plastic deformation stress concentration remains out of
question. The plastic zone extends throughout the wall when

$$p = \frac{b-a}{a}\,s_0,$$

no matter whether the pressure p is exerted inside or outside the tube.

In order to assist the reader inexperienced in the use of the plastic sector we give some other instances of its application. In a tube of square section with a symmetrical boring, plastification starts at the corners as indicated in fig. 27. But when the internal pressure is increased, the regime of plastic deformation changes, and another system of stress distribution offering less resistance to plastic flow throughout

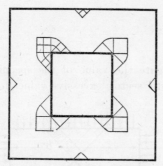

Fig. 27.—Tube of square section with equidistant boring, loaded by internal pressure to the point of plastification.

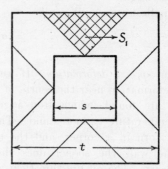

Fig. 28.—Tube of square section loaded by internal pressure until advanced plastic flow occurs.

the wall sets in, which holds until rupture occurs. This regime is indicated in fig. 28 and leads to the formula for bursting pressure

$$p_e = \frac{t-s}{s} R.$$

The wall begins to give way at the inner or outer pressure

$$p = \frac{t-s}{s} s_0,$$

but the pressure rises due to work-hardening.

We may imagine a string of clay enclosed in the indicated manner and externally compressed until plasticity occurs. The principal stress in the plane of symmetry at the top of the triangular boring shown in fig. 29 is

$$s_1 = 2k(1 + \pi/3).$$

This is not the only solution which fulfils the mathematical equations of our problem. If we have a cylinder with a triangular boring, we

may draw at each corner a region enclosed between two logarithmic
spirals and filled with identical spirals all having the centre as their
origin.

As another exercise we look at the plastic regions around a rectangular boring in a structural member of any shape under even or

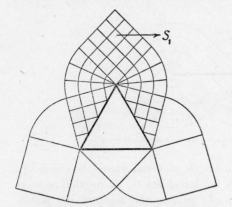

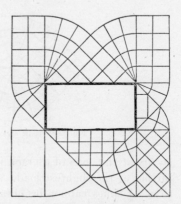

Fig. 29.—Shear-stress trajectories around a
trihedral boring in a block of plastic matter
under pressure or tension.

Fig. 30.—Above: trajectories of maximum shear stress around a duct of
rectangular section in plastic matter.
Below: trajectories of principal stress.

uneven surrounding compression (fig. 30).   The shear-stress lines between the triangular and rectangular zones are axes centred on the
corners and radii swinging through 45°.   In the lower half we have
drawn the principal stress trajectories which make angles of 45° with
the shearing-stress trajectories.

4. In a test bar with a hair-line crack across a small part of the
section, plastic regions start at the ends of the crack at the slightest

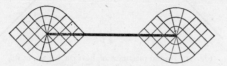

Fig. 31.—Plastic regions at the ends of an internal crack

load.   As shown in fig. 31, each region consists of 5 zones, two isosceles
right-angled triangles, two sectors of 90° and one square.   If the bar

is strained a little more, some zones unite as indicated in fig. 32.
The main principal stress in the square is

$$s_1 = s_0(1 + \pi/2) = 2 \cdot 57 s_0.$$

At the ends of a crack the plastic mass flows under a stress about
$2\frac{1}{2}$ times the yield stress. This is a remarkable fact, contrary to what

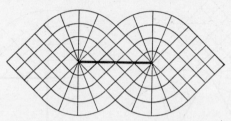

Fig. 32.—Plastic regions around a fully developed crack

occurs at the ends of a crack in brittle material where the crack rips
further at the slightest load. A reinforcement by an incision of more
than $2\frac{1}{2}$ times cannot be obtained, because the angle of the plastic
sector never exceeds $\pi/2$.

If we compare fig. 32 with fig. 16, we see that we only added a symmetrical upper half. The mathematical solution is the same.

5. Let us consider another plane problem. Fig. 33 gives the profile
of a grooved strip of infinite extent in the sense normal to the drawing.

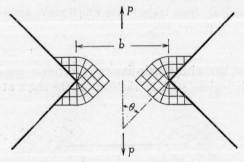

Fig. 33.—Initial plastification near the bottom of the
grooves on the broad sides of strips

Plastification begins at the bottom of the grooves as soon as the
bar is pulled.

If θ denotes the angle of the plastic sector, b the thickness at the bottom of the grooves, P the pull on the strip per unit of breadth that produces plastic flow throughout, then

$$P = 2k(1 + \theta)b.$$

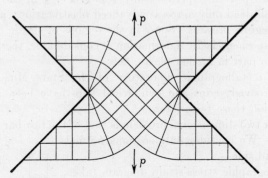

Fig. 34.—Plastified regions in grooved bars—fully developed

Fig. 34 is analogous to fig. 15 representing the wedge with a blunt edge, dealt with in Chap. IV, § 1.

When we pull a strip, grooved as indicated in fig. 35, two plastic regions are developed. What happens when the load is increased depends on the depths of the grooves and the angle. We know that grooves increase the resistance to traction in the adjacent material. If in fig. 36 $a > b(1 + \theta)$, the plastic region represented in the centre part of the figure becomes apparent. If, however, $a < b(1 + \theta)$, the straight parts of the bar are plastically strained at a lower load, and the regime shown at the top and bottom of the figure will prevail. The figure has been drawn for $a = 1.785b$ and $\theta = \pi/4$ (angle of groove 90°). In this case the yield limit is reached at the same load in the whole grooved section as in those parts of the bar which are unaffected by the grooves. Both regions may exist simultaneously. They are separated by regions which are dotted in the figure.

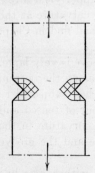

Fig. 35.—Strip with shallow grooves on broad sides.

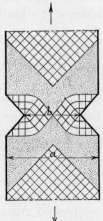

Fig. 36. — Plastified regions and trajectories of maximum shear stress in a tensile bar *with equal resistance of full and grooved section.*

We cannot be sure that these regions are exactly bounded as indicated in fig. 36. This is true only when the plastic mass is incompressible—a condition fulfilled when plastic flow occurs.

As Nadai proved experimentally (Chap. IV, § 2) the boundaries and the yield load only agree at advanced plastification; at this stage Prandtl's regime prevails. Spurs in the regions of elastic deformation develop first when elastic deformation is considerable, then they cease and take no part in further plastic flow.

In the metallographic laboratory of the State Mines extensive tests on grooved strips and cylindrical bars have been made. We shall mention these tests later.

Another two-dimensional problem is that of the test bar represented by fig. 37. We consider only sections normal to the broad side.

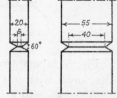

An autographic stress-strain diagram taken during the test gave the yield at a load of 9·2 tons (46 kg./mm.²), and this value was confirmed by the Amsler test machine. Plastic flow through the whole grooved section took place at this loading. From the formula

Fig. 37.—One of the test bars used to check the theory of grooved bars. The grooves must be relatively deep.

$$s_1 = s_0(1 + \theta) = s_0(1 + \pi/3) = 2 \cdot 05 s_0$$

we find for the yield stress $s_0 = 22 \cdot 5$ kg./mm.²
Ordinary test bars of the same material had given upper yield stress 24·2 kg./mm.², lower yield stress 22·5 kg./mm.² The curvature at the bottom of the groove was 0·13 mm., which, as we shall find in Chap. XXIII, § 3, has no influence.

The specific deformation at the bottom of the groove is very large. In Chap. XVI we shall show that grooved bars rip along the bottom of the grooves as square holes do in the corners when subjected to tension. There is a great difference in the behaviour of tensed and compressed grooved bars. In compressed bars the curvature in the bottom of the groove disappears at a light pressure and the groove becomes perfectly sharp.

We now proceed to the examination of the bar with a hair line crack at both sides, angle of groove zero and angle of the plastic sector 90° (fig. 38).

Plastification only occurs just beside the crack in the reduced section when the main principal stress amounts to

$$s_1 = s_0(1 + \pi/2) = 2 \cdot 57 s_0.$$

But this stress is reached at the slightest pull. When the load is sufficiently increased the plastic region is identical to that represented in
fig. 16. For further increase of load the cracks extend inward. We shall
deal with the rupture of plastic matter in Chap. XX.

6. Fig. 39 represents the small side of a broad strip in which an
athwart-placed square hole is made through the whole breadth. At
the left side the plastic region is indicated which sets in at a slight
pull, and at the right side is shown the regime that suddenly pre-
dominates when the pull is increased and leads to rupture. The ultimate yield limit is therefore calculated in the elementary way. The

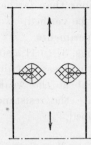
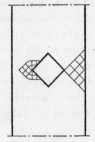
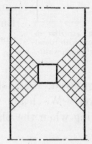

Fig. 38.—Bar in
tension, with rent-
like incisions at the
broad sides.

Fig. 39.—Bar in
tension, with a square
hole extending right
through it whose dia-
gonal is parallel to the
length of the bar.

Fig. 40.—Bar in
tension, with up-
right square hole
through full width.

sharp corner gives no reinforcement. The reason why such broad
strips may be dealt with as plane problems is that the large area above
and below the hole prevents displacement in the broad direction.

Imagine a wide strip as before with a square hole which now has
its edges parallel to those of the strip. When slightly pulled, four small
regions of plastic flow develop at the corners as shown in figs. 23, 25,
26, and 27. This is rather curious for pull in one direction, but shows
that when the material has found a satisfactory pattern of shear-stress
lines it keeps to it as long as it can. We now leave this stage of deformation. It will suffice for the designer to keep in mind fig. 40, and then
he will understand why the strength of a perforated bar of ductile
matter is calculated in the ordinary way.

When the hole is round instead of square, plastification starts in
two small zones beside the hole enclosed between logarithmic spirals,
filled with identical spirals which all have the centre of the hole as

their origin. This is explained by the fact that families of these curves
alone form orthogonal trajectories issuing at 45° from the wall of the
hole. But this regime of deformation indicated at the left side of
fig. 41 is only a transitory one. When the load on the bar is increased

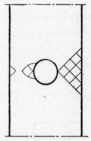

the regime drawn at the right-hand side prevails.

In order to avoid misunderstanding we repeat
that these two-dimensional solutions do not apply
to notched strips. If incisions are made at the small
sides, no special calculation needs to be made. The
lines or planes of maximum shearing stress are at
angles of 45° with the broad surfaces and the constriction takes place in the thickness only, although
somewhat more near the incisions than farther off.
But all these conclusions must be verified. No real
insight is obtained without experiments.

Fig. 41.—Bar in
tension, with round
hole through width.

It may be mentioned that figs. 31 to 41 also help
to describe the regions of plastic stress distribution
for grooved, cracked, and perforated strips bent at the weakened
section. We leave it to the reader to calculate the resistance to
bending when the plastic regions are fully developed.

7. Is a section of a bar always reinforced by small grooves, sharp
incisions, internal holes or cracks? Yes, but only under statical loading. Reloading and especially reversal of the load has a devastating
effect. We know that under the smallest load the metal flows at the
ends of cracks and at the points of sharp corners, and that the region
of plastic flow is limited in extent, contrary to what happens in elastic
deformation, where the influence of stress concentration spreads over
the whole structural member.

When the plastically strained structure is unloaded the metal in
the minute deformed regions is pushed back to its former site. The
orientation of the crystals is now different, thus these deformations
require a considerable rearrangement of atoms at each movement.
In the long run the worst treated crystals give it up. Intercrystalline
cracks occur which may unite to form larger cracks when loading and
unloading is repeated. In this way a groove, an incision, a split or a
crack may easily lead to rupture even in plastic matter.

The surface tension of molten iron is very great (950 dynes per
cm. compared with 72 for water). At red heat iron is an ideal plastic
material whose extensibility and contractility are almost unlimited.
The atoms move freely. A small crack heals. Due to surface tension,

fissures close; sharp corners become rounded. Normalizing of mild steel (heating at 900° to 950° C.), which induces recrystallization, or even annealing at a lower temperature which effaces working stresses, must be carried out in order to restore plasticity.

The thermal movement of the atoms allows rearrangement. Even at normal temperature the loss of ductility by work-hardening is in time more or less restored, but, when the melting-point of metals is approached, the damaged internal structure is rapidly cured. Silver, copper, and lead heal more easily than steel after ill-treatment.

CHAPTER VI

The Plastic Mass Compressed between Parallel Planes

1. The solution of the problem of the flattening of a plastic mass opens the road to solving many problems of technical interest. It must therefore be treated in full detail.

In this chapter we restrict ourselves to the two-dimensional problem, and first we will calculate the shape of the surface curves of the mass squeezed out from the press. Experiment confirms the conclusion that as soon as the mass leaves the press and is no longer stressed or strained, it moves in pure translation.

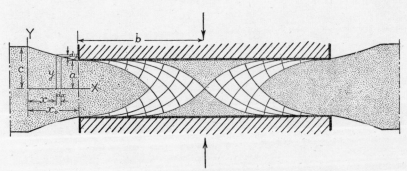

Fig. 42.—Plastic mass compressed between parallel plane surfaces

We proceed to calculate the surface curve relative to the axes X, Y moving with the mass outside the press (fig. 42).

If the upper plane descends dy, a volume $b\,dy$ leaves the press per unit of length which is equal to $y\,dx$. Thus

$$\frac{dy}{y} = -d\left(\frac{x}{b}\right),$$

$$\therefore \ \log_e y - \log_e c = -\frac{x}{b},$$

or

$$y = ae^{\frac{x_0 - x}{b}}.$$

40

The problem is to find the stresses at any point of the compressed plastic mass. The solution was given by L. Prandtl,[*] and is, with the notation shown in fig. 13,

$$s_x = -k\left(c + \frac{x}{a} - 2\sqrt{1 - \frac{y^2}{a^2}}\right),$$

$$s_y = -k\left(c + \frac{x}{a}\right),$$

$$s_s = k\frac{y}{a},$$

where c is a constant of integration.

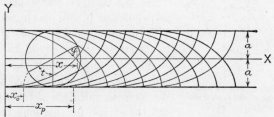

Fig. 43.—Notation for the problem of the plastic mass between parallel planes

The reader must verify whether the two partial differential equations given in Chap. I, § 2, are fulfilled so that flow takes place under internal equilibrium, and whether the condition of plasticity is satisfied, namely,

$$(s_s)_{max}{}^2 = \left(\frac{s_x - s_y}{2}\right)^2 + s_s{}^2 = k^2,$$

k being the yield shearing stress.

We must now prove that the trajectories of maximum shearing stress, which show the direction of $(s_s)_{max}$ by the direction of their tangents at each point, are two sets of cycloids. It is useful to introduce the parameter t, the angle turned through by the revolving circle. The co-ordinates expressed in terms of t (fig. 43) are

$$x = x_0 + a(t + \sin t) \quad \text{and} \quad y = a \cos t,$$

whence

$$\frac{dy}{dx} = \frac{-\sin t}{1 + \cos t}.$$

[*] *Zeitschr. f. angew. Mathematik und Mechanik*, 1923, III, p. 401; Hütte, I, 1936, *Mechanik der bildsamen Körper*, p. 347; A. Nadai, *Plasticity*, 1931, p. 221.

The stresses at the point (x, y) are found by substitution to be

$$s_x = -k(c + x_0/a + t - \sin t),$$

$$s_y = -k(c + x_0/a + t + \sin t),$$

$$s_s = k \cos t.$$

In fig. 44 we have drawn the stress circle for an arbitrary point

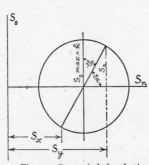

(x, y) of the plastic mass. The angles between the principal stresses and the axes are called α. However, we are not interested in α (see 2α in fig. 44), but in the direction of the maximum shearing stress $(s_s)_{max} = k$, which occurs on two perpendicular planes making angles of $45°$ with the principal directions, $\beta = 45° - \alpha$. In the stress circle we read $2\beta = 90° - 2\alpha$, double the angle which the shear-stress trajectories make with the X- and Y-axes. We have to calculate β from these data, and the excuse for this long treatment is, that in each case in which the pattern of

Fig. 44.—Stress circle for plastic flow at a point in the mass compressed between parallel planes.

the shearing-stress lines must be computed, we have to proceed in a similar way.

From fig. 44 we see

$$\tan 2\beta = \frac{s_y - s_x}{2s_s} = -\frac{\sin t}{\cos t} = -\tan t.$$

Apply $\quad \tan 2\beta = \dfrac{2 \tan \beta}{1 - \tan^2 \beta} \quad$ or $\quad \tan^2 \beta + \dfrac{2 \tan \beta}{\tan 2\beta} - 1 = 0.$

Thus $\qquad\qquad \tan^2 \beta - \dfrac{2 \tan \beta}{\tan t} - 1 = 0,$

and $\qquad\quad \tan \beta = \dfrac{1}{\tan t} \pm \sqrt{\dfrac{1}{\tan^2 t} + 1} = \dfrac{\cos t \pm 1}{\sin t}.$

Remembering that $\qquad \dfrac{\cos t - 1}{\sin t} = \dfrac{-\sin t}{1 + \cos t},$

we have $\qquad\qquad \tan \beta = \dfrac{-\sin t}{1 + \cos t} \quad$ or $\quad \dfrac{\sin t}{1 - \cos t}.$

The first expression, as we have seen when determining dy/dx, gives the direction of the tangent to the cycloid at the point t.

We have still to prove that the two sets of cycloids form a network of orthogonal trajectories.

The first set is $\qquad x = x_0 + a(t + \sin t),$

$$y = a \cos t,$$

whence $\qquad \dfrac{dy}{dx} = -\dfrac{\sin t}{1 + \cos t} = \tan \beta_1.$

The second set is $\qquad x = x_p - a(t - \sin t),$

$$y = a \cos t,$$

whence $\qquad \dfrac{dy}{dx} = \dfrac{\sin t}{1 - \cos t} = \tan \beta_2.$

It is evident that $\tan \beta_1 \tan \beta_2 = -1$, which had to be proved. We have only to keep in mind that the shear-stress lines are cycloids, and it will always be easy to go back to the stress formula.

2. For this problem as well as for the subsequent ones we suppose that the pressing surfaces are rough like a file, and that a layer of thickness equal to the height of the teeth is retained so that the plastic mass slides over itself. The resistance is then independent of pressure and equal to the yield shearing stress k over the whole surface. Even with a smooth surface this assumption holds true except for the actual ends. In fact, the pressure increases so rapidly towards the interior that, due to Admonton's law $R = fP$, where $R =$ resistance to friction, $f =$ coefficient of friction, $P =$ normal force, at a short distance from the edges, R surpasses k. The yield shearing stress is the limit of friction. As soon as this is attained, the internal pressures increase in proportion to x. The farther we move to the right in fig. 43 the greater is the total shearing force we must overcome. Let us denote by $_0 s_x$ and $_0 s_y$ the normal pressures near the sides of the press. These pressures are equal and increase proportionally to x, but in inverse proportion to a because, for a given pushing force acting to the left, the pressure must be less when the distance is larger. By this simple reasoning, we get

$$_0 s_x = {_0 s_y} = -k\left(c + \frac{x_0}{a}\right)$$

and

$$\begin{matrix} _0 s_2 \\ _0 s_1 \end{matrix} = -k\left(c + \frac{x_0}{a} \pm 1\right).$$

According to Hencky's theorem the normal and the principal stresses s_1 and s_2 increase with $2k \times \tfrac{1}{2}t$ as the tangent to the trajectories turns through $\tfrac{1}{2}t$. So we find for point t (fig. 45) the principal stresses

$$\frac{s_2}{s_1} = -k\left(c + \frac{x_0}{a} + t \pm 1\right).$$

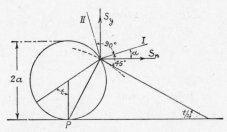

Fig. 45.—Computation of the stresses at a point on a cycloid by application of Hencky's theorem

It must be mentioned that because P is the pole of the revolving circle the tangent turns through an angle $\tfrac{1}{2}t$ as the circle rolls through angle t. The figure also indicates that

$$\tan t = \cot 2\alpha,$$

in which α means the angle which the stress s_x makes with the principal direction I, so we obtain

$$\frac{s_y}{s_x} = \frac{s_1 + s_2}{2} \mp \frac{s_1 - s_2}{2} \cos 2\alpha$$

$$= \frac{s_1 + s_2}{2} \mp \frac{s_1 - s_2}{2} \sin t$$

$$= -k\left(c + \frac{x_0}{a} + t \pm \sin t\right),$$

$$s_s = \frac{s_1 - s_2}{2} \sin 2\alpha = \frac{s_1 - s_2}{2} \cos t = k \cos t.$$

3. In solving problems on plasticity suggested by engineering practice, special attention must be paid to the boundaries of adjacent plastic zones. Not only do zones with different methods of shearing-stress trajectories alternate, but non-plastified zones may be inserted between them. These will be dotted in our figures.

We must now deal with the bung-like plastic mass which is squeezed out when the pressing planes approach each other.

In the formulæ for the stresses we meet a constant c, which still has to be determined. The mass outside the space filled with trajectories in fig. 42 must be in static equilibrium when accelerations remain out of question. We can express the stresses and co-ordinates at the boundary in terms of the parameter t.

$$s_x = -k(c + t - \sin t),$$

$$s_y = -k(c + t + \sin t),$$

$$s_s = k \cos t.$$

$$x = a(t + \sin t), \qquad y = a \cos t.$$

$$dx = a(1 + \cos t)\,dt, \quad dy = -a \sin t\,dt.$$

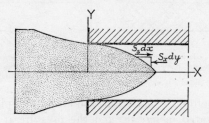

Fig. 46.—Equilibrium of the extruded band outside
the two bounding cycloids

From the equilibrium of the elementary prism indicated in fig. 46 we see that half the force pulling the bung to the right is

$$\int_{t=0}^{t=\pi/2} s_s\,dx = ka \int_0^{\pi/2} \cos t(1 + \cos t)\,dt = ka(1 + \pi/4),$$

and that half the force which pushes the bung to the left is

$$\int_{t=0}^{t=\pi/2} s_x\,dy = ka \int_0^{\pi/2} (c + t - \sin t)\sin t\,dt = ka(c + 1 - \pi/4).$$

The equilibrium of both forces requires $c = \pi/2$, and this gives the solution of the problem. But we still have to examine whether for $t = 0$ the plastic mass can carry the pressure $\dfrac{\pi}{2}k$ at the edge of the pressure planes. This is one of the most instructive problems of the theory of plasticity.

4. In fig. 47 the network of shearing-stress trajectories and the boundary of the plastified region are shown for the case where the plastic mass is pressed between perfectly lubricated planes. Along the outer lines of maximum shear stress *abc* we have the normal stress $s_n = -k$ and the shearing stress $s_s = -k$. This makes it possible that at the edge of the rough plates a pressure jumping from $s_y = 0$ to $s_y = -1\cdot57p$ may be supported. That *ac* also satisfies as a boundary line does not matter. For the slightest friction near the centre of the press the boundary *abc* is chosen.

We now return to the press with rough plates and consider the plastic mass as slightly compressible.

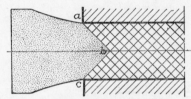

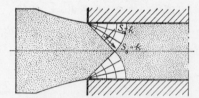

Fig. 47.—Plastic mass compressed between frictionless parallel planes

Fig. 48.—Mathematically possible maximum shear-stress trajectories for the mass between rough planes in the initial stage of plastification.

In this case before the mass starts to move, two plastic sectors will develop, as indicated in fig. 48, and the pressure at the edges must increase to

$$s_x = s_y = k + 2k\frac{\pi}{4} = 2\cdot57k.$$

This would be even greater than with perfectly smooth pressing plates

But in applied mechanics the principle holds that a deformation such as a displacement takes place in the way demanding the least external force. So before the stage of fig. 48 is reached the mass moves as shown in fig. 46, because this only requires a pressure $s_y = 1\cdot57k$ in place of $s_y = 2\cdot57k$ as needed for the development of plastic sectors.

It must be added that any other boundary line than the cycloid will give a solution for which the conditions of equilibrium are fulfilled. But the solution we have adopted is that for which the total pressure is lowest.

5. We still have to examine the almost-triangular non-plastified regions near the line of symmetry in fig. 42. The shearing stress along the planes just beside the centre line and along the centre line itself must be zero. But along the bases of the triangular sections shearing stresses gradually develop, and sliding of the mass occurs when $s_s = -k$. The central zones stick to the sides of the press. It may easily be proved that the dotted zones are in equilibrium under the stresses along the borders and that nowhere is the critical stress $s_s = k$ reached.

When the pressing planes approach, the four dotted zones shrink. The plastic zones predominate and swallow the elastic zones. The resulting force exerted by the press to squeeze out the plastic mass as a function of a may now be calculated by the reader. The pressure to which lead, copper or Armco-iron gaskets must be subjected are determined in this way. We come back to the subject at the end of Chap. XIV.

6. For a question of plastic flow dealt with in a later chapter we need the solution of another problem, namely, that of a mass pulled by two parallel plates (fig. 49). Perhaps this case may only be realized when sufficient surrounding pressure is superposed. But as only differences of principal stresses are taken into account, we can calculate just as well with tensional stresses.

A curious point in this problem is that when reversing the forces, the boundaries between plastic and elastic regions change. This is a warning not to assume analogies between the solutions of problems in elasticity and plasticity.

With the notation of fig. 43 we now obtain for the cycloids

$$x_1 = x_0 + a(t - \sin t), \quad y_1 = -a \cos t,$$

$$x_2 = x_p - a(t + \sin t), \quad y_2 = -a \cos t;$$

and for the stresses at point t:

$$s_x = k(-1{\cdot}57 + x_0/a + t + \sin t),$$

$$s_y = k(-1{\cdot}57 + x_0/a + t - \sin t),$$

$$s_s = -k \cos t;$$

and at point (x, y):

$$s_x = k\left(-\frac{\pi}{2} + \frac{x}{a} + 2\sqrt{1 - \frac{y^2}{a^2}}\right),$$

$$s_y = k\left(-\frac{\pi}{2} + \frac{x}{a}\right),$$

$$s_s = -k\left(\frac{y}{a}\right).$$

It is not astonishing that fig. 49 has a different appearance from fig. 42. The thrust and the sliding along the planes is reversed; the right side of fig. 42 has become the left side of fig. 49. It may be proved

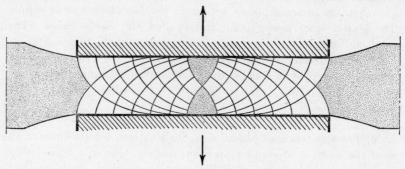

Fig. 49.—The plastic mass drawn between rough parallel planes

that the dotted regions are in equilibrium under the stresses acting, on the boundaries. Fig. 49 is only a snapshot of what happens. When the plates are withdrawn the cycloids grow, the material is drawn in and plastified, the cup-like zones grow in size.

We continue the investigation of this problem in Chap. VIII.

CHAPTER VII

The Plastic Mass Compressed between Inclined Planes

Since Prandtl treated the problem of the plastic mass squeezed between parallel planes, others have solved more complicated cases of plastic flow. We owe to Nadai the solution of the problem of the stress distribution in a wedge-shaped plastic mass.*

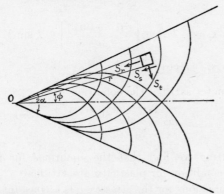

Fig. 50.—The plastic mass compressed between the sides of a widening dihedral angle

As the displacements of the particles are a function of their position with respect to the rough walls, the shear-stress trajectories must be a set of curves growing as their distance to the line of intersection of the planes increases. The simplest solution will be in polar co-ordinates (fig. 50), and must satisfy the equations of internal equilibrium

$$r \frac{\partial s_r}{\partial r} + \frac{\partial s_s}{\partial \phi} + (s_r - s_t) = 0,$$

$$\frac{\partial s_t}{\partial \phi} + r \frac{\partial s_s}{\partial r} + 2s_s = 0,$$

* *Zeitschr. für Physik.*, 1924, p. 125; *Handbuch der Physik*, Vol. VI, 1928, p. 475, 23 d.

and the condition of plasticity

$$\left(\frac{s_r - s_t}{2}\right)^2 + s_s{}^2 = k^2.$$

This condition may be expressed in terms of a parameter θ as was done when dealing with the problem of parallel planes,

$$s_s = k \cos \theta, \quad \frac{s_r - s_t}{2} = -k \sin \theta.$$

By drawing the stress circle it is clear that the parameter is double the angle which the tangent to the trajectory makes with the radius. The solution of the differential equations gives

$$s_r = -kc \log_e \left[\frac{r^2(c - \sin \theta)}{a^2}\right] + k \sin \theta,$$

$$s_t = -kc \log_e \left[\frac{r^2(c - \sin \theta)}{a^2}\right] - k \sin \theta,$$

$$s_s = k \cos \theta,$$

when the parameter satisfies the condition

$$d\phi = -\tfrac{1}{2} \frac{\sin \theta}{c - \sin \theta} d\theta.$$

By substituting we find that the equations for internal equilibrium and the condition for plasticity are satisfied.

In these expressions for the stresses, c is a constant which depends on the dihedral angle 2α, and a^2 is the integration constant, which must be determined by a condition of the problem. In general we know where the pressure is zero.

The calculation of the co-ordinates ϕ and r expressed in terms of the parameter θ is as follows:

We calculate ϕ by integration of the last given expression,* and r by taking into account that the maximum shearing stresses make angles of 45° with the principal stresses.

The angles between the tangents to the trajectories and the radii therefore are

$$\tan \beta_1 = \frac{-\cos \theta + 1}{\sin \theta} \quad \text{and} \quad \tan \beta_2 = \frac{\cos \theta + 1}{\sin \theta}.$$

* Compare Hütte, 1926, p. 94, formulæ 33 and 30.

The result of the integrations is

$$\phi = \frac{c}{\sqrt{c^2-1}} \arctan\left\{\sqrt{\frac{c+1}{c-1}}\tan\left(\frac{\pi}{4}-\frac{\theta}{2}\right)\right\} - \frac{\frac{\pi}{2}-\theta}{2},$$

$$r = b\sqrt{\frac{c-1}{c-\sin\theta}}\exp\left[\frac{\pm 1}{\sqrt{c^2-1}}\arctan\left\{\sqrt{\frac{c+1}{c-1}}\tan\left(\frac{\pi}{4}-\frac{\theta}{2}\right)\right\}\right].$$

Let us comment on this result:

1. For the line of symmetry $\phi = 0$, $\theta = \pi/2$ and $s_s = 0$.

2. From the expression $s_s = k\cos\theta$ it is clear that we touch the walls for $\theta = 0$ and for $\theta = \pi$, because along the walls we find $s_s = \pm k$.

3. We call the angles which the bisector makes with the planes, half the dihedral angle $\pm \alpha$.

This allows us to compute c for several dihedral angles, noting that at the wall the expression for ϕ becomes

$$\alpha = \frac{\pi}{4} - \frac{c}{\sqrt{c^2-1}}\arctan\sqrt{\frac{c+1}{c-1}}.$$

This gives:

$c = 1$	$c = 1\cdot1922$	$c = 2$	$c = 5$
$\alpha = \pi$	$\alpha = \dfrac{\pi}{2}$	$\alpha = 24°\,17'$	$\alpha = 6°\,15'$

The extreme case we shall consider in detail will be $c = 1\cdot1922$ which means that the dihedral angle will be $180°$, and the planes unite. Figs. 50 and 51 are drawn for $c = 2$, $\alpha = 24°\,17'$.

2. Our solutions are for statical problems, and the pictures of shear-stress trajectories must be considered as snapshots. The lines are identical in the case where the angle opens on its hinge (the plastic mass being pressed into the wedge-shaped space), and in the case where the plastic mass is pressed through a narrowing mouthpiece in order to extrude it as a strip. In both cases the mass moves along the walls in the same direction.

We assume that only the walls of the nozzle are rough. Then the axial component of the speed is the same for each point of extreme

trajectory, as may be seen from fig. 51. This is true both at the en-
trance to and at the exit from the plastic zone, because in front of and
behind this zone the mass behaves like a block of solid matter. As
it moves the compressed mass suddenly enters the region of plastification, where it is thoroughly kneaded.

The axial velocity increases as the nozzle narrows. After extrusion
the mass behaves like a solid strip and moves with a much higher
translation speed than when entering the nozzle. The energy spent in
transforming block to strip is removed as heat.

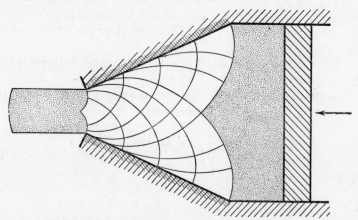

Fig. 51.—Extrusion of a plastic mass through a rough mouthpiece

We only mention the case in which the mass becomes steadily
thicker as it proceeds through the nozzle. This case leads to the reversal of some signs in our formulæ, but the picture of stress lines
changes a good deal.

3. When the angle between the planes increases the theory remains
valid. For $\alpha = \pi/2$ and $c = 1{\cdot}1922$, the planes unite.

The shear-stress trajectories change into a family of spirals starting
tangentially to the plane at the origin, and ending normal to the plane,
as shown in fig. 52.

As a variation to fig. 51 we have shown in fig. 53 how a block of
plastic material might be pressed to a strip through a slot in the wall
by hydraulic pressure. Rough walls are indicated by double shading,
smooth by ordinary shading.

As to the trajectories, it makes no difference whether the force is
obtained by a plunger as indicated in fig. 50 or by hydraulic pressure

as shown in fig. 53. Here the dotted part of the block is elastically deformed in an incalculable manner, but this does not affect the correctness of our solution for the region of plastic flow.

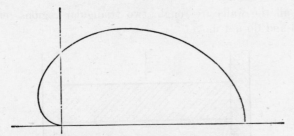

Fig. 52.—One of the trajectories of maximum shear stress in the plastic mass extruded through a slot in the wall

Cold-rolled or extruded profiles are subject to manufacturing stresses which may approach the yield limit. This may be visualized by grinding or filing away the outer fibres at one side. The bar then

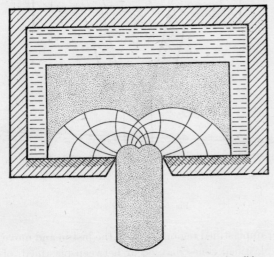

Fig. 53.—Plastic mass forced through a slot in a rough wall by hydraulic pressure

bends. Metals such as lead, copper, brass and light alloys are shaped to profiles or tubes by means of the extruding press. Iron is rolled, but as the block is red-hot, and the atoms in this state move freely, the manufacturing stresses occur when cooling.

4. The problem of the paste-spout is so important in manufacturing artificial silk, cellophane, thermoplastics, ceramics, macaroni and in other industries, that we give in fig. 54 another instance of a mouthpiece. We note:

1. If all the walls are rough, two triangular regions remain unplastified and do not move.

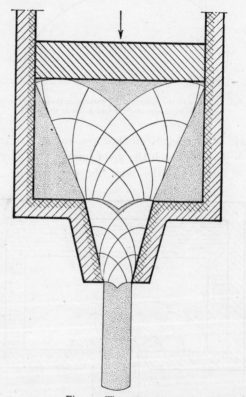

Fig. 54.—The paste-spout

2. Other unplastified regions stick to the piston and move on with it.

3. Non-plastified zones may occur between plastified, of which the shear-stress lines belong to different sets of curves, as shown in the middle of fig. 54.

Numerous experiments have been made on the flow of a plastic mass through an opening.* The best and most instructive are those

---

* The most recent experiments are enumerated at the end of the article of H. Unckel, *Zeitschr. f. techn. Physik*, 22, 1941, No. 10, p. 34.

of H. Tresca,* who, nearly half a century ago, showed that these experiments may be made with red-hot iron, as well as with lead or clay. The agreement of theory and practice is sufficiently good when we take into account the condition of the walls.

The reader should draw the boundary of the plastic region for the case of fig. 54, where the mouthpiece is made less acute, and observe that here the walls are nowhere the envelopes of the trajectories, as they always are when the plastic mass slides along them.

Another exercise is to check that the lines of maximum shearing stress are logarithmic spirals when the nozzle is perfectly smooth. The solution of this problem is given in Chap. II.

5. The rolling of sheets is a combination of the problems treated in both this and the former chapter. At the left of fig. 55, where the sheet is thin, the plastic region is enclosed between two parallel tangents to the rollers, and at the right, where the sheet is thick, the plastic region is enclosed between two tangents to the rollers which form a dihedral angle. These regions join at the point where the limiting members of both families of curves meet at angles of 45° with the axis of symmetry. At the left side of the figure these curves are the cycloids studied in the former chapter, at the right they are the curves dealt with in this chapter.

Neither the thin part of the sheet nor the thick part suffers any deformation at the moment

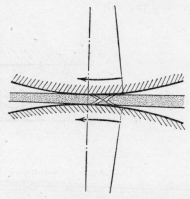

Fig. 55.—The rolling of sheet metal between rollers or of grease between wheel teeth

shown on this snapshot, and we may see two dotted, nearly triangular regions which stick to the rollers. The steel is only kneaded in the regions filled with trajectories.

When the metal is cold-rolled, lasting rolling stresses may be detected. Compressive stresses occur in the surface layers. Such steel is very strong, for reasons we shall discuss later on.

---

* " Mémoire sur l'écoulement des corps solides ", *Mémoires de l'Académie des Sciences*, XX, 1872, p. 281.

CHAPTER VIII

The Outer Regions of Plastic Deformation in the Mass Compressed between Parallel Planes

1. We may now go on with the further examination of the problem treated in Chap. VI. We have first to investigate the deformation of the outer regions, which we called the bungs, in the case where these bungs remain between the pressing planes, so that they are also compressed (fig. 56).

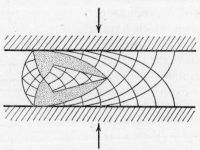

Fig. 56.—Plastic zones in the outer regions of the mass compressed between parallel planes

A simple test with putty, dough or clay compressed between two boards, or still better a piece of hot iron under the pressing hammer, shows that the ends are bounded by quadrants of circles.

The principal stresses at the surface are $s_1 = s_0$ and $s_2 = 0$. We know from the theory given in Chap. II, that the shearing-stress trajectories are logarithmic spirals. In the true cylindrical shape of the surface we detect the principle of self-adjusting. Indeed, if the surface had somewhere a smaller radius of curvature, the pressure towards the interior would rise more rapidly, and the material would have greater strength. A larger radius of curvature would act oppositely.

In the interior of the bung the material is compressed as in a closing beak. The jaws hinge at the line of symmetry in the throat.

The trajectories in the dihedral angle comply with all the conditions of this problem. The extreme trajectories of this family meet the extreme logarithmic spirals at an angle of 45° with the line of symmetry.

In the former chapter we dealt with the open wedge-shaped space. We drew attention to the difference in pattern of the shear-stress lines shown in this instance. The bung divided into two plastic and two non-plastic regions, and was in equilibrium under the same shearing and normal stresses at its boundaries as the uncompressed bung shown in fig. 46 and dealt with in § 3, Chap. VI.

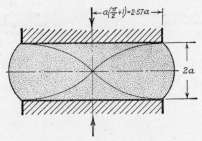

Fig. 57.—The plastic mass compressed between parallel planes without development of plastified zones

2. In order to improve our understanding of the flow of matter with cycloidal trajectories in the plastic zones between the bungs and cup-like central region, we now suppress these zones which were essential in figs. 42 and 43, so that the dotted outer and inner regions become adjacent (fig. 57). We suppose that the ends are properly rounded off beforehand. This is an instance among many others of a single shear-stress trajectory. Another such line may be seen in the middle of fig. 117.

Generally the plastic region is absent only a single moment. As soon as the pressing planes approach so that the breadth of the test piece becomes more than 2·57 times its thickness, plastic regions arise.

3. In fig. 58 we show the case where the block is pressed over a breadth equal to its thickness by rough pressing planes. There is no plastic region. We can at most say that only along two planes at 45° to the principal directions is the critical shearing stress attained. Even when the planes approach no plastic regions develop.

At a breadth between one and 2·57 times the thickness of the block, we have the case shown in fig. 59. Instead of the well-known plastic

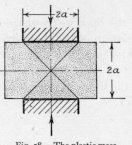

Fig. 58.—The plastic mass with slip planes at an angle of 45° to the pressing planes.

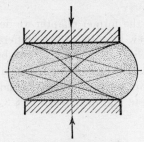

Fig. 59.—The plastic mass with curved slip planes tangent to the dihedral angle.

regions, we have only two curved surfaces to which the dihedral angles dealt with in Chap. VII are tangential.

CHAPTER IX

Plastification in the Annular Space between Two Concentric Cylinders, caused by Relative Translation. Clay-cutting with a Wire

1. The space between two concentric cylinders is filled with a plastic mass, such as an unguent or butter. The problem is to find the stress distribution and lines of maximum shear stress when, as indicated by the arrow in fig. 60, one cylinder moves with respect to the other. The construction of the trajectories, originating tangentially at one cylinder wall and striking the other normally, is due to two mathematicians.* The problem is analogous with that treated in Chap. VI. At the top we must have a non-plastic zone resembling the central part of fig. 42, and at the bottom one that is similar to the cup-like central part of fig. 49. The reader may now guess the form of the trajectories.

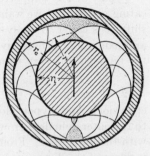

Fig. 60.—Trajectories of maximum shear stress in the annular space between concentric cylinders caused by relative translation.

We may assume that the plastic mass is compressed at the top and pulled at the bottom. And, indeed, if the interspace between flat pressing planes is curved to a ring, the trajectories become two sets of epicycloids and hypocycloids intersecting orthogonally, which provide the exact solution. The mathematical expressions for the radial and tangential tensions are complicated. The expression in polar coordinates for the shearing stress at any point of the mass in plastic flow is simpler and of more interest (fig. 60). It is

$$s_s = \frac{r_e^2 + r_i^2 - 2\dfrac{r_e^2 r_i^2}{r^2}}{r_e^2 - r_i^2} k.$$

* C. Caratheodory and E. Schmidt, *Zeitschr. für angewandte Mathematik und Mech.*, Vol. 3 (1923), p. 468.

If in this formula for r we substitute r_i or r_e we find $s_s = \pm k$. Along the rough cylinder walls the yield shearing stress prevails. For

$$r = \frac{2r_e^2 r_i^2}{r_e^2 + r_i^2}$$

we have $s_s = 0$.

The trajectories cut this circle at angles of 45°. The points of the non-plastified polar caps sticking to the cylinders are also situated on this cylinder.

The simplest way for the engineer to get an exact insight into the stress distribution is the application of Hencky's theorem. Along the walls and the neutral circle the pressure increases in proportion to the centre angle. We recommend the graphical treatment.

If we have to deal with the most common practical problem, that of a shaft at rest supported in a bush by a cylindrical layer of lubricating grease, and we want to calculate at what pressure it begins to shift, it is easier to apply the formulæ given in Chap. VI by means of approximation. These give the limit for the stress distribution where the interspace is very thin.

2. If we increase the radius of the rolling circle describing the epicycloids and hypocycloids, the upper non-plastified zone sticking to the outer cylinders grows quickly and for $r_e = 2 \cdot 83 r_i$ (fig. 60) unites with the lower zone. From this diameter on, the phenomenon is independent of the distance to the outer wall. The neutral wall with regard to shearing stresses, where $s_s = 0$, is given by $r = \frac{4}{3} r_i$, and facilitates the construction of fig. 61. Here we have a snapshot of the translation of a cylinder through a solid block of plastic matter. We often see the polar caps still sticking to the wires used for cutting clay.

It must be clearly understood that our theory does not exactly correspond to practice. We imagined a superposed encompassing pressure of sufficient magnitude to close the cut behind the wire. Non-deaerated clay is compressible. The flow of the material agrees fairly well with theory for the case of a round stem ploughing through clay. Experience with brick-making machinery and briquetting of patent fuel improves our insight into plasticity.

3. The simplest plasticity problem is the stress distribution in the layer of grease between two parallel planes sliding over each other. We think of the mixture of tallow, stearine, engine oil and soap between the standing and sliding ways for ship-launching, or of grease between crosshead and guide in a sliding mechanism. In fig. 62 the shear-stress trajectories are drawn. The principal stress trajectories are not indi-

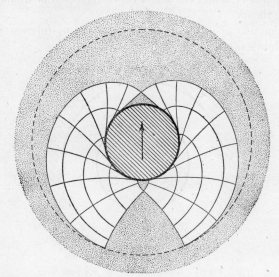

Fig. 61.—Clay-cutting with a wire

cated; they make angles of 45° with the greased surfaces. The resistance to friction is independent of the superposed encompassing pressure c and of the thickness of the layer of oil. The principal stresses are $s_1 = c + 2k$ and $s_2 = c$.

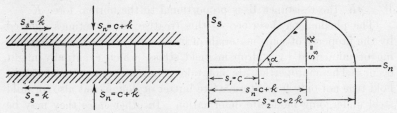

Fig. 62.—Lubrication of two parallel plane surfaces with grease

It might be of some use to observe that if the surfaces are curved, so that we have to deal with concentric cylinders turning in each other as indicated in fig. 63, the shear picture alters completely. There we have indicated that the plastic mass sticks to the outer cylinder.

The same takes place when the inner cylinder slides axially. When grease in a tube is driven forward under pressure, the mass moves as a whole. This is the case of central lubrication, so much in vogue in modern machinery, where the longer tubes must be dimensioned according to this theory.

The behaviour of unctuous lubricants is quite different from that of viscous lubricants.

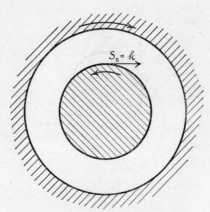

Fig. 63.—Grease between axle and bush
rotating in opposite directions

We deal in this book with statical problems only. The speed of flow which dominates the stress distribution in viscous liquids is not considered.

The law of friction at surfaces lubricated with grease differs also from that for dry friction, where according to the law of Admonton $W = fK$, the resistance W is proportional to the normal force K.

The phenomena described in this treatise are sometimes affected by the property of some materials of being reinforced by work-hardening or influenced by a drop in yield stress, which eventually might occur. These properties are not taken into account. Our formulæ hold true not only for materials like butter or dough, but also for mild steel undergoing moderate deformation. In other cases they may be considered as a first approximation.

CHAPTER X

Three-dimensional Plasticity

1. For the transition from the elastic to the plastic state, the three principal stresses, or more accurately their three differences, are equally responsible. To understand the plasticity criterion a good beginning is to study the equilibrium of a tetrahedron formed by a Cartesian trihedral angle on the principal directions and an arbitrary plane of reference. The stresses are represented by Mohr's device, and it may be proved that the stress on any plane is represented by the co-ordinates s_n and s_s, this point being situated in the sickle-shaped space between the three circles drawn on the principal stresses. We recommend the reader to compare the following exposition with the classic theory of three-dimensional stress.

We imagine an elementary cube in the plastic mass with its edges along the principal directions, so that the faces are submitted only to the principal normal stresses s_1, s_2 and s_3, and we cut this cube by a plane normal to a diagonal. Now we compute the stresses on the triangle which forms the base of the cut-off tetrahedron (fig. 64) and find

$$s_n = \frac{s_1 + s_2 + s_3}{3},$$

$$s_{sc} = \tfrac{1}{3}\sqrt{(s_1 - s_2)^2 + (s_2 - s_3)^2 + (s_3 - s_1)^2}.$$

It is easier for the reader to calculate this himself than to follow a direct computation which we might give. By s_{sc} we indicate that this shearing stress is characteristic for the plasticity problem. By permutation of the suffixes we see that the stresses on the eight sides of the inscribed octahedron (fig. 65) are all the same. On four sides the shearing stress has, for instance, the direction indicated in fig. 64 (bottom right), and on four other sides the shearing stress is symmetrical. In general s_{sc} is not perpendicular to an edge of the octahedron. This is only so in the very important case when two principal stresses are equal. When one of the principal stresses is the mean of the extreme stresses, then s_{sc} is parallel to an edge. In Chap. XXIII, § 12,

63

a graphical construction for s_{sc} (this is $\frac{1}{3}s_0\sqrt{2}$) is given which may be useful in checking the principles here stated.

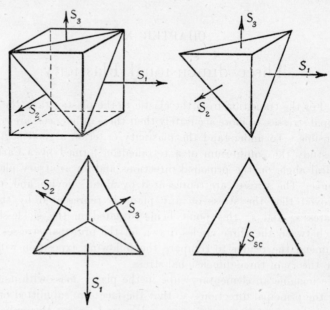

Fig. 64.—The principal stresses on the sides of an elementary cube and the computation of the stresses on the inscribed octahedron

The characteristic shearing stress is not the greatest. This occurs on conjugate planes which have the mean principal direction as line of intersection and make angles of 45° with the extreme principal stresses.

For rupture the greatest specific elongation is the criterion, but plastic yield depends, as we shall see, on a somewhat complicated specific distortion for which this characteristic shearing stress is responsible. Modern physics made it possible to calculate the cohesion of simple substances, but the computed strength is about ten thousand times that which is revealed by a tensile test.

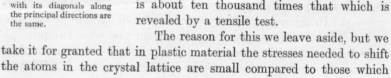

Fig. 65.—The stresses on all sides of the octahedron with its diagonals along the principal directions are the same.

The reason for this we leave aside, but we take it for granted that in plastic material the stresses needed to shift the atoms in the crystal lattice are small compared to those which break the cohesion. We consider the cohesive forces between the particles as invincible, and in the following calculations we superpose the general pressure

$$-s_n = \frac{s_1 + s_2 + s_3}{3},$$

so as to keep the volume of the element considered constant. On our octahedron we have only left the shearing stresses, and we may now examine the distortion due to these stresses alone.

It has been proved by experiment that plastic yield is provoked by shearing stresses independent of general tension or compression. The subject in hand requires some mental exertion. In order to ease this, we begin with two simple cases, that of pure tensional stress and that of pure shearing stress as met in a bar subjected to pure torsion.

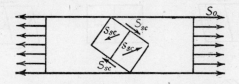

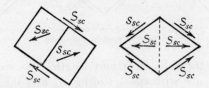

Fig. 66.—Cube in a tensile bar with its diagonal along the axis of the bar

2. The four diagonals of the cube make angles of $\phi = 54° \ 44' \ 8''$ with the principal direction ($\cos^2 \phi = \frac{1}{3}$). These diagonals are normal to the sides of the octahedron. Beside these four planes subjected to the characteristic pure shearing stress

$$s_{sc} = \tfrac{1}{3}\sqrt{(s_1 - s_2)^2 + (s_2 - s_3)^2 + (s_3 - s_1)^2},$$

there are in general innumerable other planes subjected to the same shearing stress but accompanied by normal stresses of different magnitude.

We now consider the case of pure tensional stress and imagine a cube placed with one diagonal in the tensional direction (fig. 66). For reasons of symmetry in space the edges make angles of 54° 44′ with the main principal direction. The normal stress on all the sides is $s_n = s_0/3$ and the shearing stress $s_{sc} = \tfrac{1}{3}s_0\sqrt{2}$. The values are the same for this cube as for the octahedron placed with a diagonal along the same line, and indeed for all the planes whose normal makes an angle of 54° 44′ with that direction. When we superpose a general pressure $s_n = -s_0/3$ the normal stress disappears. The cube or octahedron remains subjected to the same shearing stresses on the sides directed to both opposite vertices. This causes a curious deformation, a sharpening of the vertices and an elongation of the diagonal, but the volume remains constant. We shall calculate the distortion of the cube, the change of angles, the specific elongation of the diagonal and the energy of deformation.

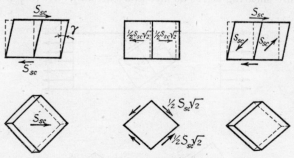

Fig. 67.—Distortion of a cube in a tensile bar in consequence of the shear stresses on the sides

The edges of the cube have unit length. We calculate first the obliquity of the cube with the aid of fig. 67 and then the elongation of the diagonal. The horizontal displacement of the top right corner with relation to the lower corner is $\gamma = s_{sc}/G$, in consequence of the shearing stress s_{sc} on the top and bottom surfaces. The horizontal components of the shearing stress on the sides are $\tfrac{1}{2}s_{sc}\sqrt{2}$. Add to this a relative displacement of the extreme vertical ribs $\tfrac{1}{2}\dfrac{s_{sc}}{G}\sqrt{2} \times \tfrac{1}{2}\sqrt{2} = \tfrac{1}{2}\dfrac{s_{sc}}{G}$, so that the total relative horizontal displacement of the ends of the diagonal in consequence of the shearing stresses on the eight sides of the octahedron is $\dfrac{3s_{sc}}{2G}$. From this we find that the specific elongation of the diagonal d for the cube shown in fig. 68 amounts to

$$\epsilon'' = \sqrt{\tfrac{1}{3}} \times \frac{s_{sc}}{G}\sqrt{\tfrac{3}{2}} = \tfrac{1}{2}\frac{s_{sc}}{G}\sqrt{2} = \frac{s_0}{3G}.$$

This is not the total elongation. To find that we have to add the specific elongation due to the change in volume.

We are in search of the physical principle which underlies the condition of plastic yield in space. It is most important to remember that the deviation from the right angle which the perpendiculars between top and bottom surface make is

$$\gamma = \frac{s_{sc}}{G} = \tfrac{1}{3}\frac{s_0}{G}\sqrt{2}.$$

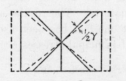 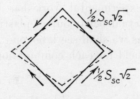

Fig. 68.—Specific elongation in a tensile test, due to shear stresses only

We now calculate the deviation which another right angle in the plane of symmetry undergoes in consequence of the components $\tfrac{1}{2}s_{sc}\sqrt{2}$ on the sides of the cube (fig. 68), and we find this $s_{sc}/(\sqrt{2}G)$, which being less than s_{sc}/G is not characteristic.

The Criterion of Plasticity.

When the tension bar is loaded to the yield limit s_0,

$$s_{sc} = \tfrac{1}{3}s_0\sqrt{2} = \tfrac{1}{3}\sqrt{(s_1 - s_2)^2 + (s_2 - s_3)^2 + (s_3 - s_1)^2}.$$

We call this value s_{sc} on the sides of the octahedron the critical shearing stress or *the criterion of plasticity*.

The physical meaning, as we shall find later on, is that plastic yield occurs when the deviation of the former perpendiculars uniting top and bottom surfaces of the cube from the right angle reaches

$$\gamma = \frac{s_{sc}}{G} = \tfrac{1}{3}\frac{s_0}{G}\sqrt{2}.$$

We must bear in mind the formula $\gamma = s_{sc}/G$ as the criterion of plasticity.

The relative shift of four sets of sides of the octahedron must be taken in the direction of s_{sc}. At pure tension the material yields when $s = s_0$. Then the yield shear stress is

$$s_{sc} = \tfrac{1}{3}s_0\sqrt{2} = \tfrac{1}{3}\sqrt{(s_1 - s_2)^2 + (s_2 - s_3)^2 + (s_3 - s_1)^2},$$

or $$2s_0{}^2 = (s_1 - s_2)^2 + (s_2 - s_3)^2 + (s_3 - s_1)^2 = \text{constant},$$

or $$s_0{}^2 = s_1{}^2 + s_2{}^2 + s_3{}^2 - s_2s_3 - s_3s_1 - s_1s_2 = \text{constant}.$$

This function of the principal stresses alone is decisive for plastic yield. The expression was first formulated by Maxwell [*] and much later again proposed by Huber, Hencky and Von Mises.

Much experimental work has been done to test the agreement with the actual behaviour of plastic material. The results are rather confused, as we shall see later on. But one fact has been ascertained. The first yield for each combination of principal stresses occurs when

$$s_0{}^2 = s_1{}^2 + s_2{}^2 + s_3{}^2 - s_2s_3 - s_2s_1 - s_1s_2.$$

This has been proved by the classical tests of Ross and Eichinger [†] and those of Stromeyer.[‡] It has been confirmed by Kist,[§] who made

[*] See *Origin of Clerk Maxwell's electric ideas, as described in familiar letters to William Thomson*, edited by Sir Joseph Larmor, Cambridge, 1937, pp. 32–3.

Extract from letter dated 129 Union Street, Aberdeen, 18th Dec., 1856 (we use our own notation). " Here is my present notion about plasticity of homogeneous amorphous solids: Let ϵ_1, ϵ_2 and ϵ_3 be the 3 principal strains at any point, s_1, s_2 and s_3 the principal stresses connected with ϵ_1, ϵ_2 and ϵ_3 by symmetrical linear equations, the same for all axes. Then the whole work done by s_1, s_2, s_3 in developing ϵ_1, ϵ_2, ϵ_3 may be written: $A = a(s_1{}^2 + s_2{}^2 + s_3{}^2) + b(s_2s_3 + s_3s_1 + s_1s_2)$, where a and b are coefficients, the nature of which is foreign to our inquiry. Now we may put: $A = A' + A''$, where A' is due to a symmetrical compression ($\epsilon_1' = \epsilon_2' = \epsilon_3'$) and A'' to distortion without compression ($\epsilon_1'' + \epsilon_2'' + \epsilon_3'' = 0$) and $\epsilon_1 = \epsilon_1' + \epsilon_1''$, $\epsilon_2 = \epsilon_2' + \epsilon_2''$, $\epsilon_3 = \epsilon_3' + \epsilon_3''$. It follows that

$$A' = \tfrac{1}{3}(a + b)(\epsilon_1 + \epsilon_2 + \epsilon_3)^2$$

$$A'' = \frac{2a - b}{3}(\epsilon_1{}^2 + \epsilon_3{}^2 + \epsilon_3{}^2 - (\epsilon_2\epsilon_3 + \epsilon_3\epsilon_1 + \epsilon_1\epsilon_2)).$$

"Now my opinion is that these two parts may be considered as independent, A' being the work done in condensation and A'' that done in distortion. Now I would use the old word ' resilience ' to denote the work to be done on a body to overcome its elastic forces.

"The cubical resilience R is a measure of the work necessary to be expended in compression in order to increase the density permanently. This must increase rapidly, as the body is condensed, whether it is wood or lead or iron. The resilience of rigidity R_2 (which is the converse of plasticity) is the work required to be expended in pure distortion in order to produce a permanent change of form in the element. I have strong reasons for believing that when $s_1{}^2 + s_2{}^2 + s_3{}^2 - s_2s_3 - s_3s_1 - s_1s_2$ reaches a certain limit ($s_0{}^2$), then the element will begin to give way."

[†] Berichte No. 14 and 28 der Eidgen. Material-Prüfungsanstalt, Zürich, 1926 and 1928.

[‡] An experimental comparison of simple and " compound " stresses, *Engineering*, 15th Sept., 1916, p. 268.

[§] " Theoretische beschouwingen en proeven ter bepaling van de draagkracht van gelaschte constructies ", *De Ingenieur*, 1934, B, 172.

use of other measurements, and very remarkable was the agreement with the results of the specially devised experiments of Bijlaard.* Our own experiments, which we shall mention in the next chapter, were most convincing.

Let us now calculate the energy of distortion of the cube shown in fig. 67, loaded to the yield shearing stress on its six sides. Assume that the cube is fixed at the left corner, then the work done by the force on the top side is

$$A_1'' = \tfrac{1}{2}s_{sc} \times \frac{s_{sc}}{G} = \frac{s_{sc}^2}{2G},$$

and by the horizontal components of s_{sc} on the lateral sides

$$A_2'' = \tfrac{1}{4}s_{sc}\sqrt{2} \times \frac{\tfrac{1}{2}s_{sc}\sqrt{2}}{G} = \frac{s_{sc}^2}{4G}.$$

In general it is not allowed to add energy of distortion, but it is allowed in this case where the forces do no work due to the displacement of their working point by other forces. The total energy of distortion is therefore

$$A'' = \tfrac{3}{4}\frac{s_{sc}^2}{G},$$

$$A'' = \frac{1}{12G}\left\{(s_1 - s_2)^2 + (s_2 - s_3)^2 + (s_3 - s_1)^2\right\}.$$

This is the expression for the energy of distortion obtained by removing the energy of change of density from the total energy of deformation, as was done by Maxwell. The material yields at the moment the expression reaches the critical value. We may say it yields when $s_{sc} = \tfrac{1}{3}s_0\sqrt{2}$ or when the distortion of all the opposite sides of the octahedron reaches a value $\gamma = s_{sc}/G$. The reader may choose the criterion he prefers. Each leads to the same expression:

$$(s_1 - s_2)^2 + (s_2 - s_3)^2 + (s_3 - s_1)^2 = 2s_0^2 = \text{constant},$$

or
$$s_1^2 + s_2^2 + s_3^2 - s_2 s_3 - s_3 s_1 - s_1 s_2 = \text{constant}.$$

3. We now carry out a similar calculation for another extreme case, that of pure shear stress as realized in a twisted cylindrical bar. The principal stresses $s_1 = s$, $s_2 = 0$, $s_3 = -s$, are indicated in

---

* *De Ingenieur*, 1933, B, 129: " Weerstand van een verzwakte doorsnede van een getrokken plaat, berekend volgens de hypothese van Huber-Hencky."

fig. 69, which also shows the elementary cube for which we examine the deformation. The normal to the upper side of the cube makes an angle of 54° 44′ with the mean principal stress ($\cos^2$ 54° 44′ = $\frac{1}{3}$) and by reason of symmetry the angles with both other principal stresses are the same; therefore these also make angles of 54° 44′ with the normal. The shear tension on the upper side is the characteristic shear tension and the material yields when

$$s_{sc} = \tfrac{1}{3}\sqrt{(s_1 - s_2)^2 + (s_2 - s_3)^2 + (s_3 - s_1)^2} = \tfrac{1}{3}s\sqrt{6}.$$

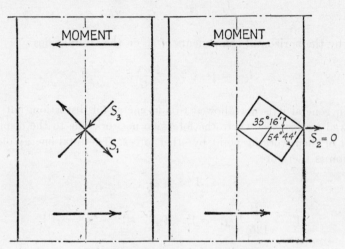

Fig. 69.—Elementary cube in a twisted bar

We know from the tension test described in § 2 that

$$s_{sc} = \frac{s_0}{3}\sqrt{2},$$

hence

$$s = \frac{s_0}{\sqrt{3}} = 0.578 s_0.$$

In the case of pure shear $s_1 = -s_3 = (s_s)_{\max}$.

We find thus

$$(s_s)_{\max} = \frac{s_0}{\sqrt{3}} = 0.578 s_0$$

in agreement with the plasticity-criterion of Maxwell, Huber, Hencky, and Von Mises, and somewhat different from that of Coulomb-Guest who had accepted

$$(s_s)_{\max} = 0.5 s_0.$$

Let us for the moment adhere to Maxwell, whose criterion is so well proved by experiment.

Now we calculate the stresses on the six sides of our cube in the classical way, and therefore we start by computing the angles which the normals to these sides make with the principal directions. The squares of the cosines are:

$$\cos^2 \alpha_1 = 0{\cdot}6222 \qquad \cos^2 \alpha_2 = 0{\cdot}3333 \qquad \cos^2 \alpha_3 = 0{\cdot}0445$$

$$\cos^2 \beta_1 = 0{\cdot}3333 \qquad \cos^2 \beta_2 = 0{\cdot}3333 \qquad \cos^2 \beta_3 = 0{\cdot}3333$$

$$\cos^2 \gamma_1 = 0{\cdot}0445 \qquad \cos^2 \gamma_2 = 0{\cdot}3333 \qquad \cos^2 \gamma_3 = 0{\cdot}6222.$$

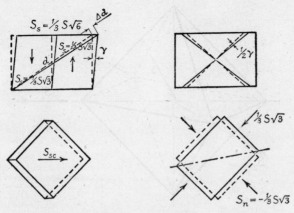

Fig. 70.—Elastic deformation of an elementary cube in a twisted bar

With the well-known formulæ *

$$s = s_1 \cos^2 \alpha + s_2 \cos^2 \beta + s_3 \cos^2 \gamma$$

$$s_s^2 = (s_1 - s_2)^2 \cos^2 \alpha \cos^2 \beta + (s_2 - s_3)^2 \cos^2 \beta \cos^2 \gamma \\ + (s_3 - s_1)^2 \cos^2 \gamma \cos^2 \alpha,$$

taking into account

$$s_1 = s, \quad s_2 = 0, \quad s_3 = -s,$$

we find for the top and bottom, for which the middle column holds,

$$s_0 = 0, \quad s_s = \tfrac{1}{3}s\sqrt{6},$$

and for the lateral surfaces the values shown in fig. 70. As indicated in the upper corner of fig. 70 on the right, in this case as well as in the

---

* Klopper: *Leerboek der Toegepaste Mechanica*, tweede deel, p. 198.

former the deviation of the angles of the perpendiculars between top and bottom is simply

$$\gamma = \frac{s_{sc}}{G},$$

but now this is
$$\gamma' = \frac{1}{3}\frac{s}{G}\sqrt{6}.$$

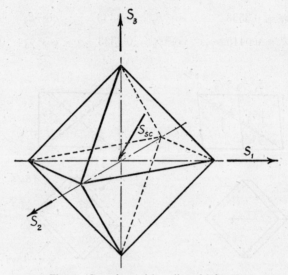

Fig. 71.—General case of three-dimensional stress

In order to investigate the problem thoroughly, in search for more analogies, we calculate the deviation which the originally right angle, indicated at the bottom right of fig. 70, undergoes in consequence of the normal stresses on the sides $s_n = \pm \frac{s}{3}\sqrt{3}$. We find $\gamma' = \frac{2}{\sqrt{6}}\frac{s_{sc}}{G}$, which is less than γ and different from what we found in the former case (§ 2).

When we calculate the specific elongation of the diagonal of the cube, we find

$$\epsilon'' = \frac{1}{3}\frac{s_{sc}}{G}\sqrt{2} = \frac{2}{9}\frac{s_0}{G}.$$

Although the relative sliding of upper and lower sides is the same, the specific elongation of the diagonal is only $\frac{2}{3}$ of what we found in the former case. We can also calculate the greatest specific elongation and shortening in any direction at the point under consideration. We find that these occur along the axes of the octahedron corresponding to the extreme principal stresses. They are $\epsilon = s_0/4G$, which is $\frac{3}{4}$ of what we found before.

Every deformation except the deviation of the right angles by $\gamma = s_{sc}/G$ is different in these extreme cases, and the general case is situated between them.

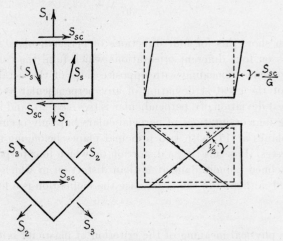

Fig. 72.—The elementary cube serving to compute the distortion
of the elementary octahedron

4. We now come to the general case, that of three different arbitrary principal stresses shown in fig. 71. We know that the material yields when the sides of the octahedron are subjected to normal stress

$$s_n = \frac{s_1 + s_2 + s_3}{3},$$

and shearing stress

$$s_s = \tfrac{1}{3}\sqrt{(s_1 - s_2)^2 + (s_2 - s_3)^2 + (s_3 - s_1)^2} = \tfrac{1}{3}s_0\sqrt{2}.$$

This shearing stress in general is neither normal, nor parallel to a side of the equilateral triangle.

Imagine a cube cut from the plastic mass at the spot under examination that has two opposite sides coinciding with opposite sides of the octahedron. This cube (fig. 72) is turned until the shearing stress on top and bottom s_{sc} is directed towards a corner. For these two sides we have the above-mentioned normal stress and shear stress. On the vertical sides the stresses are different although we may remark that the component of a shearing stress on the vertical sides, directed towards an edge common with the top or bottom, is $\frac{1}{2}s_{sc}\sqrt{2}$. But this is somewhat away from the point.

Again we have the deviation of the perpendiculars given by

$$\gamma = \frac{s_{sc}}{G} = \frac{s_0}{3G}\sqrt{2}.$$

We can show this for four directions of perpendiculars as we can take cubes on four different orientations which fulfil the condition of having two sides coinciding with opposite sides of the octahedron.

γ is not the greatest deviation of any perpendicular at the spot. The greatest deviation of a perpendicular is $(s_1 - s_3)/2G$, and is not met with along four orientations of perpendiculars but only occurs for two pairs of planes at 45° with two principal planes belonging to the extreme stresses. It seems that a distortion by which four perpendiculars become inclined is more dangerous than distortion in which only two are inclined, although in the latter case the inclination is a little more.

5. The physical meaning of the criterion of plasticity is that yield sets in when the four normals to the sides of the elementary octahedron deviate by the angle $\gamma = s_{sc}/G$ from the usual position.

It is easiest to picture this rather complicated distortion by means of an octahedron held in the hand.

For pure shear stress, when s_{sc} is directed along a common edge, we find that one of the diagonals of the octahedron is lengthened, another is shortened, and the third remains unaffected. This is the state most susceptible to plastic distortion.

When two principal stresses are equal, which means that by superposing a general pressure of opposite sign we have to deal with linear stress, then the shearing stresses are directed towards opposite vertices of the octahedron. It will be proved later on that in this case the critical value s_{sc} is reached with the smallest stress difference, let us say at the least constraint. With pure shear stress the difference of the extreme principal stresses at the moment the yield starts is a maximum $s_1 - s_3 = 1{\cdot}156 s_0$, while for linear stress it is $s_1 - s_2 = s_0$ only, this being the stable state of plastic flow.

When by arbitrary three-dimensional stress the yield point is attained, the octahedron turns, not bodily but mathematically; its position becomes stabilized as soon as linear stress is attained (the first case treated in this chapter, § 2). We shall explain this in a subsequent chapter, and recommend the reader when he comes to the end of the book to return to this paragraph and check it by means of the graphical method given in Chap. XXIII, § 12.

CHAPTER XI

The Ideal Yield Stress

1. Usually one of the principal stresses, the mean stress which is normal to the surface of our structural part is zero. For instance, the stress computation for bars and shafts gives the normal stress s_n and the shear stress s_s.

We can formulate an expression for the ideal principal stress s_i, i.e an imaginary tension stress which gives the same safety factor for plastic yield as s_n and s_s combined.

Mohr's stress circle shows that the extreme principal stresses are

$$\begin{matrix} s_1 \\ s_3 \end{matrix} = \frac{s_n}{2} \pm \sqrt{\frac{s_n^2}{4} + s_s^2}, \quad \text{while} \quad s_2 = 0.$$

Let us first introduce the idea of an ideal shear stress. This is

$$s_{si} = \tfrac{1}{3}\sqrt{(s_1 - s_2)^2 + (s_2 - s_3)^2 + (s_3 - s_1)^2}.$$

The safety factor is the same as with the ideal stress s_i when

$$s_{si} = \frac{s_i \sqrt{2}}{3}.$$

In our case $s_{si} = \tfrac{1}{3}\sqrt{2(s_n^2 + 3s_s^2)}$, hence $s_i = \sqrt{s_n^2 + 3s_s^2}$.

We remember that when the Coulomb-Guest criterion for plastic flow is retained (and as we shall see there are strong reasons to do so), we have
$$s_i = \sqrt{s_n^2 + 4s_s^2}.$$

And when we take the greatest specific elongation as responsible for plastic flow (which is certainly wrong, being a criterion for rupture), we reckon with

$$s_i = \frac{m-1}{2m} s_n + \frac{m+1}{2m} \sqrt{s_n^2 + 4s_s^2},$$

where $1/m$ stands for Poisson's ratio.

The difference in dimensions of the construction calculated according to Coulomb and according to Maxwell's premise is almost negligible, and in using Coulomb's criterion we are on the safe side.

2. The best experiments made to test the criterion for yield now generally adopted, are mentioned in Chap. X, § 2. We now give some test methods used by the author which are cheap to carry out and yet convincing.

In every section of the thin cylindrical part of the test bar shown in fig. 73 we find the same maximum shear stress in the neutral layer (fig. 74), viz:

$$(s_s)_{\max} = \frac{4}{3}\frac{D}{\pi r^2}.$$

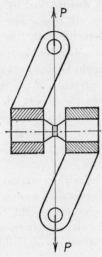

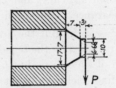

Fig. 74.—Yield shearing stress is reached simultaneously in the neutral layer and at the whole periphery of the normal section at a distance of 0·578r from the middle section.

Fig. 73.—Shear test on mild steel

At the periphery of the circle for the fibre corresponding to the angle ϕ the tangential shear stress is

$$s_s = \frac{4}{3}\frac{D}{\pi r^2}\sin\phi,$$

and the normal stress $s_n = \frac{4}{\pi}\frac{D}{r^2}\frac{x}{r}\cos\phi,$

where x is the distance to the middle.

The ideal stress at the periphery of the section at distance x therefore is

$$s_i = \frac{D}{\pi r^2}\sqrt{4^2\left(\frac{x}{r}\cos\phi\right)^2 + 3\left(\frac{4}{3}\sin\phi\right)^2}.$$

At the section $\qquad x = \dfrac{r}{\sqrt{3}} = 0\cdot578r,$

the ideal principal stress attains the same value as in the whole neutral layer, and we may expect a marked yield when

$$s_i = s_0, \quad s_{si} = 0\cdot578 s_0.$$

And indeed the upper yield stress determined with this test and with the tensile bar agreed perfectly. We took an autographic record in which yield occurred at 2190 kg./cm.² It was marked by a vertical drop to 1855 kg./cm.², and then the line slowly rose. The result on first appearance seemed in perfect agreement with the formula $s_i = \sqrt{s_n{}^2 + 3s_s{}^2}$. But the lower yield point was a few kg./cm.² lower than was revealed by the tensile test. This might be due to the common dispersion of such tests, but most observers present got the impression that the first yield really set in according to the theory of Maxwell, known as Huber-Hencky's hypothesis, but the load dropped immediately to the value calculated with the lower yield stress and then was in better agreement with the ideal tension calculated according to Guest's law.

We note that at the transition from cylindrical to conical neck the cones must be tangent to the beam of equal resistance to bending.

The reader well versed in applied mechanics, might make the objection that we based our calculation on the elementary theory which assumes that in the neutral layer the shear stress is evenly distributed over the width and is

$$s_s = \frac{4}{3}\frac{P}{A}$$

where P is the shearing force and A the area of the surface of the section. It is known that the complete theory, which takes into account the cambering of the section, shows that the shearing stress also depends on y, the distance to the centre line.

For the neutral layer

$$s_s = \frac{P}{A}\left\{\tfrac{3}{2} - \tfrac{1}{2}(y/r)^2\right\}.$$

The mean value is $\qquad s_s = \frac{4}{3}\frac{P}{A}$

but the shear stress increases from P/A at the sides to $1\cdot5P/A$ at the centre line. Nevertheless, the less accurate result is confirmed by experiment.

It is interesting to note that the smallest plastic yield effaces such subtle differences in stress distribution. The theory of plasticity helps a good deal in forming an opinion as to the necessity for using the higher theories of applied mechanics in strength calculations on steel structures.

3. In plasticity questions experiment is the mother of truth. The test represented in fig. 75 is arranged to let nature decide which criterion of plasticity is right. The test bar is bent and twisted. According to Coulomb-Guest, the ideal bending moment is $M_i = \sqrt{M^2 + T^2}$, wherein M is the bending moment and T the twisting moment. From this formula the bar must yield at the thin end, where the diameter is 10 mm. If the criterion of Huber-Hencky were exact, yielding must set in at the section where, according to the formula $M_i = \sqrt{M^2 + \frac{3}{4}T^2}$, the highest tension is reached. This must be at the thick end, where the diameter is 13·2 mm.

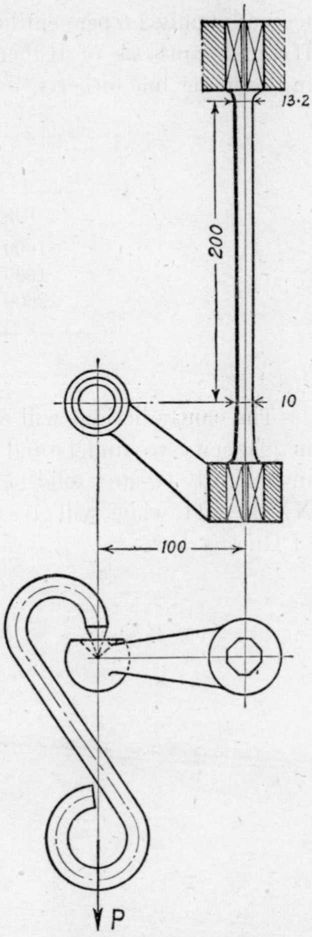

On blank test bars a careful observer sees where yield starts first. In former years, for checking theories of elastic breakdown, we used bars which the smith had kept red-hot for some minutes, and we noticed where the scale first flawed. Nowadays we use special brittle lacquers prepared to demonstrate the zones where the yield stresses are first reached.

Experiments of this type on polished test bars do not confirm Huber-Hencky's hypothesis. The bar twists suddenly at the thin end where the diameter is 10 mm. The result is in agreement with the criterion of Guest-Coulomb. For the calculation of solid shafts the first formula for the ideal bending moment must be applied.

Fig. 75.—This test was intended to make nature decide between the criterion of plasticity of Maxwell-Huber-Hencky and that of Coulomb-Guest.

4. The result is not new. It had been ascertained by many careful tests. We only refer here to those of Smith (*Engineering*, 12th March, 1909, p. 351) for solid bars submitted to torque and compression. At East London College of the University of London, he found a difference of only 2·6 per cent between the highest and lowest ideal tension. If the hypothesis of Huber-Hencky had held, we should have read in the upper line either $s_s = 1500$ kg./cm.^{2} or $s_i = 2245$ kg./cm.^{2}

s_n	s_s	s_i
0	1295	2590
−1000	1200	2610
−1660	1075	2540
−2600	0	2600

All in kg./cm.^{2}

The contradictions will clear up when we are sufficiently advanced in plasticity to understand somewhat better the stress distribution in a slightly twisted solid bar. This problem will be discussed in Chap. XXIII, § 11, which will give more experimental evidence on the validity of Guest's law.

CHAPTER XII

The Thick-walled Sphere and Wire-drawing

1. The first application of the theory of plasticity in a case of three-dimensional stress will be very easy. In the thick-walled sphere we have only to deal with one differential equation as there is only one unknown. We use fig. 9, which now represents the section of a sphere.

The vertical equilibrium of half the sphere with radius r provides

$$\pi r^2 s_r - \pi a^2 p = \int 2\pi r s_t dr$$

or

$$2rs_r + r^2 \frac{ds_r}{dr} = 2rs_t,$$

i.e.

$$ds_r = 2(s_t - s_r) \frac{dr}{r}.$$

In the direction normal to the plane of the drawing, the tension is s_t as well. For reasons of symmetry s_r and s_t are principal stresses. When two principal stresses are equal, the difference between these principal stresses and the third is limited to the yield stress, as is the case in the tensile test. So we have $s_t - s_r = s_0$. Our differential equation therefore becomes $ds_r = 2s_0 dr/r$, and the solution is

$$s_r = 2s_0 \log_e r + C.$$

The constant is determined for the ball bulging under internal pressure by the condition that at the external surface, i.e. for $r = b$, the tension is $s_r = 0$. So the result is $s_r = -s_0 \log_e (b/r)^2$, and the pressure $p = -s_0 \log_e (b/a)^2$.

Cut in any meridian section the trajectories for shear stress are the well-known logarithmic spirals crossing the radii and circles at angles of $45°$. In cases of three-dimensional stress Hencky's theorem fails. The method by which it has been deduced only applies to two-dimensional or plane problems.

Fig. 10 represents the plastification around a spherical cavity in the zone occupied by logarithmic spirals.

When our formula given above is combined with the stress formula mentioned in textbooks on elasticity for the tensions in thick-walled spheres, the extent of the region around a cavity in a plastic mass subjected to pressure or tension from all sides may be calculated.

2. We now refer briefly to wire-drawing. When the die is perfectly lubricated (fig. 76) it can exert a normal pressure only.

The theory of wire-drawing is reduced to the consideration of a solid angle of the thick-walled sphere. It is instructive to verify that counterpull in wire-drawing decreases the pressure on the wall of the

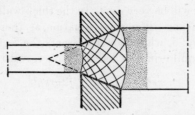

Fig. 76.—Wire-drawing through a frictionless die

die. By this means friction and wear are lessened. But disregarding friction, the work done in wire-drawing remains the same. Its equivalent is spent in heat.

A complicated subject in the theory of plasticity is the question of residual stress set up by cold-working. It may be supposed that when the pull ceases, a wire drawn through a well-lubricated die is free of tension. But in dry wire-drawing we approach the plasticity problem represented in section in fig. 51, and it may be proved that, when the wire leaves the die and solidifies, the tension stress at the surface is lower than at the interior, and after manufacture when the pull is taken off we have a wire with compression stress in the exterior fibres. This is a different quality from work-hardening, and it is also an improvement. Both qualities disappear when the wire is annealed. It then behaves as if it were made of a different material.

CHAPTER XIII

On the Tendency of the Mean Principal Stress to be Equal to either the Greatest Principal Stress or the Smallest

1. Although a problem of three-dimensional stress, the foregoing question, the stress distribution in the hollow sphere, was reduced to a single equation with only one unknown. But in all other problems of axial symmetry, we have to deal with unknown axial and radial stresses in the meridian plane, an accompanying shear stress and the third principal stress, the tangential stress normal to the meridian plane.

There are thus four unknowns, and for the solution we have available only the conditions that an element is in equilibrium in the axial and the radial directions, and also the condition of plasticity. We want one more equation, for which we must have recourse to experiment. In this case the natural law which helps us out of the difficulty is often used in applied mechanics. Although never proved, it may be granted on general grounds that, when free to choose, nature shows a preference for the solution which makes the structure give way at the least load.

The condition of plasticity is

$$s_{sc} = \tfrac{1}{3}\sqrt{(s_1 - s_2)^2 + (s_2 - s_3)^2 + (s_3 - s_1)^2} = \tfrac{1}{3}s_0\sqrt{2}$$

or

$$(s_1 - s_2)^2 + (s_2 - s_3)^2 + (s_3 - s_1)^2 = 2s_0^2,$$

i.e.

$$s_1^2 + s_2^2 + s_3^2 - s_2 s_3 - s_3 s_1 - s_1 s_2 = s_0^2.$$

We have now to answer the question: if s_2 cannot be determined by the conditions of internal equilibrium and the condition of plasticity, what value will it take in order to reduce the stresses s_1 and s_3 (or rather their difference and in consequence of this the exterior forces) as much as possible? Let us assume for a moment that s_1 and s_3 are given for a certain point in the plastic mass and s_2 is variable but bound to s_1 and s_3 by the above relation. Now let us represent the shear stress s_s on the octahedron as a function of s_2 as drawn in fig. 77, the curve being a hyperbola.

As soon as the mass yields s_s has the fixed magnitude $s_{sc} = \frac{1}{3}s_0\sqrt{2}$, s_1 and s_3 are not constant but s_{sc} is.

The figure shrinks as much as possible, s_1 and s_3 (or rather their difference) become as small as possible when $s_2 = s_1$, or when $s_2 = s_3$. Since s_s must reach the value s_{sc} with the least effort, it must take an extreme position either to the right or to the left so that $s_1 - s_3$ becomes least.

We may ask what is the distance to the origin from which we measure the magnitude of the three principal stresses. But this dis-

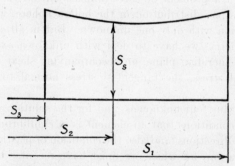

Fig. 77.—The characteristic shear stress s, as a function of the medium principal stress s_3, when the extreme principal stresses s_1 and s_3 are fixed.

tance must remain unknown. The condition of plasticity only speaks of stress differences. A superposed surrounding pressure or tension does not affect the phenomenon. Also in the state of plane stress, when the axis of revolution wanders to infinity, s_2 becomes equal to one of the extreme principal stresses for the same reason. Matter cannot abstain from obeying this law, which has important and remarkable consequences. For instance, the magnitudes of the deformations in plastic flow no longer depend on the principal stresses; they increase as long as there is room to flow. From now on we must look on the state of plastic flow as a new state of aggregation which is situated between the solid and the liquid state.

Everyone knows that when the yield point is passed matter is lengthened in the direction of s_1 and shortened in the direction of s_3. What everyone does not know is that it flows freely in the direction of s_2, and that the deformation takes place without increase of stress.

It is to this quality that the word " plastic " is due, meaning " able to be formed or moulded ".

As soon as s_2 becomes equal to s_1 or to s_3 the plastic matter flows unrestrictedly. In mild steel the flow only ceases when, by work-hardening, the yield limit is so much raised that the exterior forces no longer overcome the resistance.

But as generally there is a considerable drop in the resistance of our steel when s_2 jumps to s_1 or drops to s_3, a good deal of deformation may be observed before an increase of external force is needed for further deformation. With butter, dough or clay, some extra deformation does not affect the yield point. These are ideal substances for demonstrating plastic flow and for observing the drop in resistance when two principal stresses equal.

Sometimes s_2 jumps from the one extreme value to the other at adjacent spots in our structural part. The reader will meet this particularity in later applications. He is invited to check that when $s_2 = s_1$ or $s_2 = s_3$, the criteria of Maxwell and of Coulomb become identical. The applicability of Coulomb's hypothesis, which De Saint Venant had accepted on account of Tresca's experiments, is now explained. The laws of Maxwell and Coulomb are not in contrast but agree. The material yields as soon as Maxwell's law is fulfilled and then the resistance drops and plastic flow occurs according to the maximum shear theory. Maxwell's law always holds.

We shall find further experimental evidence of this aphorism in Chap. XXIII, § 11, dealing with the torque on a solid bar. By actually carrying out Meldahl's graphical construction for s_{si} or s_i when the principal stresses are given, as shown in Chap. XXIII, § 12, the reader will soon realize that matter flows most readily when s_2 takes an extreme value.

CHAPTER XIV

The Disc Plastometer

1. In fig. 78 is shown the compression test on a disc of clay. Prior to the test the diameter was 100 mm., thickness 15 mm. The clay was de-aerated. The arrangement resembles Scott's plastometer on which an extensive literature exists.*

We expect a likeness to the two-dimensional problem (figs. 42, 43, &c.). Indeed, if we increase the diameter, the stress distribution at

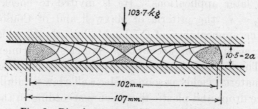

Fig. 78.—Disc plastometer used for determining the yield shearing stress of clay

the periphery must tend to identity. With the notation shown in fig. 79 equilibrium in the radial and vertical directions gives rise to the equations

$$\frac{\partial(s_r r)}{\partial r} + r\frac{\partial s_s}{\partial z} - s_t = 0$$

and

$$r\frac{\partial s_z}{\partial z} + \frac{\partial(rs_s)}{\partial r} = 0.$$

When we draw the stress circle we see that the principal stresses are

$$\begin{matrix} s_1 \\ s_3 \end{matrix} = \frac{s_r + s_z}{2} \pm \sqrt{\left(\frac{s_z - s_r}{2}\right)^2 + s_s^2} \quad \text{and} \quad s_t = s_2.$$

Here

$$\sqrt{\left(\frac{s_z - s_r}{2}\right)^2 + s_s^2} = k$$

---

* J. R. Scott: *Trans. Inst. Rubber*, 7 (1931), 169; R. L. Peek: *J. Rheol.*, 3 (1932), 345; H. L. v. Nonhuys: *Recueil Trav. Chim. des Pays Bas*, 61 (1942), 2 Février.

is the yield shear stress. We know from the previous chapter that in plastic flow the mean principal stress is equal to one of the extreme principal stresses, so that

$$s_t = \frac{s_z + s_r}{2} \pm k.$$

Now because s_t may jump from one extreme to the other at adjacent points, and as a matter of fact adjusts itself in the mean to what is wanted for flow at the least pressure, the first differential equation containing s_t is of no use.

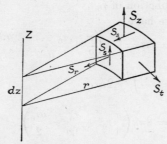

Fig. 79.—Notation for the case of rotational symmetry

We rewrite the second equation

$$r \frac{\partial s_z}{\partial z} + s_s + r \frac{\partial s_s}{\partial r} = 0,$$

and make use of two hints towards the solution. The first is that probably the simplest solution will be right; the second, that the farther we go from the centre, the more the solution must approach that of Chap. VII for the plane problem.

$s_s = \mp kz/a$ is the simplest solution that fulfils the conditions, as for $z = 0$, $s_s = 0$, and for $z = \pm a$, $s_s = \mp k$ as in the two-dimensional problem.

Our differential equation simplifies to

$$\frac{\partial s_z}{\partial z} = \frac{kz}{ra},$$

which gives the solution

$$s_z = -k \left(\frac{\pi}{2} + \frac{r_0 - r}{a} - \frac{z^2}{2ra} \right)$$

7

because we prescribed that when r_0 is large compared with a and z our formula must be identical with that found for the two-dimensional case.

Combined with the condition of plasticity, which may be written $s_r = s_z - 2\sqrt{k^2 - s_s^2}$, we find the radial tension

$$s_r = -k\left(\frac{\pi}{2} + \frac{r_0 - r}{a} - \frac{z^2}{2ra} + 2\sqrt{1 - \frac{z^2}{a^2}}\right).$$

With this kind of plastometer the total force P is measured as a function of the radius r_0 to which the disc is extended. We thus have to calculate P as a function of r_0.

At the surfaces we have

$$s_r = s_z = -k\left(\frac{\pi}{2} + \frac{r_0 - r}{a} - \frac{a}{2r}\right)$$

and

$$P = -\int_0^{r_0} s_z 2\pi r \, dr$$

$$= 2\pi k\left(\frac{\pi}{4}r_0^2 + \frac{r_0^3}{6a} - \frac{ar_0}{2}\right).$$

This calculation is not quite exact for the centre part where cup-shaped non-plastified material sticks to the pressing planes. We shall apply a correction, but first we draw attention to the remarkable fact that if we consider the difference $s_z - s_r$ and the shearing stress s_s, the expressions are identical to those found in the two-dimensional problem. Hence the trajectories of maximum shear stress are again ordinary cycloids.

The reader may ascertain for himself that for horizontal sections, the trajectories of maximum shear stress are logarithmic spirals.

2. We now consider the disc (fig. 80) of radius $r_0 = (\pi/2 + 1)a$. In this case only the descriptive lines of the cup-shaped mass are left out of the sets of cycloids. We calculate the force P for this mass by integrating the vertical stress and the shearing stress along its surface.

$$P = -\int 2\pi r(s_z \, dr - s_s \, dz).$$

We express r and z as functions of the parameter of the cycloid:

$$r = (2\cdot 57 - t - \sin t)\,a, \quad z = a\cos t,$$

and we find

$$P = 2 \times 7\cdot 85\pi ka^2 = 49\cdot 5ka^2.$$

Without taking into account the existence of a non-plastified centre core we should have found $P = 42ka^2$. The difference $7 \cdot 5ka^2$ is unimportant for a disc with a diameter greater than $5 \cdot 14a$ and negligible for a disc of the diameter we have shown in fig. 78. But we can add $7 \cdot 5ka^2$ to the approximate formula and make the result correct.

Looking again at fig. 80, we may put the question as to what the difference might be if the pressing planes were perfectly lubricated instead of perfectly rough. In the first case the yielding pressure would be $s_z = 2k$ at any point, hence

$$P_0 = 2\pi kr_0{}^2 = 41 \cdot 5ka^2, \text{ as } r_0 = 2 \cdot 57a.$$

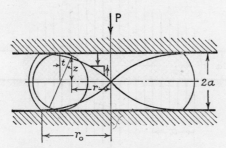

Fig. 8o.—Disc compressed to plastic yield for the case $r_0 = 2 \cdot 57a$

The difference compared with the critical force on the rough pressing planes $P = 49 \cdot 5ka^2$ is unimportant, but increases very rapidly as the diameter of the plastic disc increases.

In actual practice the pressing planes are neither rough nor perfectly lubricated, so that there is always some friction. It is easy to see that in view of the increase of pressure towards the interior, the pressure generally will be large enough to make $s_z f > k$, where f is the coefficient of friction. This means that even with rather smooth surfaces, our formula holds true.

Clay is subject to work-hardening as some water is squeezed out. Nevertheless, or perhaps for this reason, our experiments were in good agreement with tests made on the same clay by ball indentation.

An experimental proof of the soundness of our theoretical investigation is found in the literature for a disc with a diameter of $2 \cdot 57$ times the thickness.*

* *Zeitschrift für technische Physik*, 1924, No. 9, " Ueber die unter einer Belastung sich bildenden Gleitflächen ", p. 376, fig. 56.

3. In this paragraph we may insert a remark on the behaviour of plastic packing; for instance, a gasket of lead or of copper wire flattened between the flanges, as indicated in fig. 81.

The pressure at a distance x from the edge (Chap. VI) is

$$s_n = k\left(\frac{\pi}{2} + \frac{x}{a}\right).$$

The linear increase is shown in the figure. As a matter of fact the distribution of pressure near the centre is slightly different, but this may be neglected.

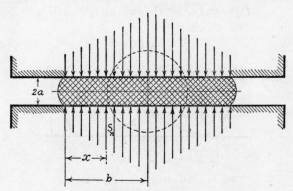

Fig. 81.—Distribution of stress on a band of plastic packing
flattened from an originally round cross-section

The force on the packing-ring per unit of length is

$$P = 2k\int\left(\frac{\pi}{2} + \frac{x}{a}\right)dx = k\left(\pi b + \frac{b^2}{a}\right),$$

and the mean pressure for which the bolts must be calculated,

$$p = \left(\frac{\pi}{2} + \frac{b}{2a}\right)k,$$

where b is half the width of the flattened gasket, a half the thickness, and k half its yielding pressure.

It is evident that when the bolts are tightened b increases and a decreases, so that the resistance to pressure rapidly increases, even at constant yield pressure $2k$, and more so when the packing is subject to work-hardening. But other qualities than plasticity are essential in packing, e.g. the coefficient of thermal expansion must be the same as that of the flanges. The theory of plasticity explains why soft packing enclosed in a groove is very suitable.

It is important to note that deformation stops as soon as equilibrium between stresses and imposed pressure is reached. Unfortunately, in many materials, especially metals, the atoms may continue to alter their relative positions under pressure, the more so as we approach the melting-point. This phenomenon, called *creep*, although a subdivision of plasticity, is beyond the scope of this treatise.

4. At some distance from the edge, the pressure on the pressing planes increases no matter how good the lubrication. Although a drop in yield pressure marks the upper yield point (and a compression test on a steel prop is instructive), we wish to examine also the yield under compression independent of the influence of the tangential surface stress dealt with in this chapter. The author made some successful experiments on the upper and lower yield points of mild steel under compression with round test pieces as shown in fig. 82, and found about the same values as in tension tests, although the figures seemed to be somewhat lower.

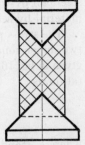

Fig. 82.—Shear-stress trajectories in a specially devised compression test.

The trajectories of maximum shear stress are traced under the assumption of perfect friction between hardened cone and mild steel cup. This friction was obtained by painting the surfaces with a suspension of fine carborundum powder in glue.

The reader can only understand such a problem if he is well acquainted with the stress circle for this kind of stress distribution.

CHAPTER XV

The Brinell Hardness Test

1. The simplest plastometer, of vast application, is the hardened steel ball by which an indentation is made in the surface of the plastic material by a known load.

The stress problem and the delimitation of the plastic zones for the two-dimensional case have been solved by Prandtl.* The result is given in fig. 16. We found that the pressure, needed to make an indentation, is

$$p = \left(1 + \frac{\pi}{2}\right)s_0 = 2 \cdot 57 s_0,$$

where s_0 stands for the yield stress. Plastic deformation extends over a width of $3b$ if the width of the punch is b.

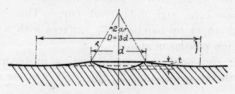

Fig. 83.—Ball indentation

When the ball test is made on the polished surface of a mild-steel test piece, it may be observed that the surface becomes dull over a circle of diameter about $D = 3d$, d being the diameter of the indentation. Outside the indentation the material rises slightly, but on the average by not more than $\frac{1}{8}$ of the crater's mean depth. Near the brim the emergence is greatest as is shown in fig. 83.

Before going farther, let us examine the plastic zone under an annular part of the surface with uniform loading (fig. 84). At the

---

* Proceedings of the First International Congress for Applied Mechanics, Delft, 1924, "Spannungsverteilung in plastischen Körpern", p. 50.

moment of plastic yield the vertical pressure p is the main principal
stress and in the ring described by the revolution of the isosceles right-
angled triangle the trajectories of maximum shear stress must be the
straight lines indicated in fig. 84.

When a pressure is exerted outside and inside the annular surface

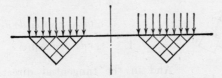

Fig. 84.—Shear-stress trajectories under an
annular surface loaded to yield of the underlying material.

with diameters D and d until the free surface emerges, the shearing
stresses in the solid will be symmetrical. We can guess that fig. 85
represents a section through the plastic zones with shear-stress trajectories for the ball indentation, but only the calculation can give a
decisive answer. It is certain that under the ball a central cone is

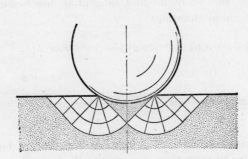

Fig. 85.—Plastified region for the Brinell ball test

pushed downward with a vertical angle of 90° and that in the plastic
ring of triangular section, the vertical and horizontal principal stresses
are $s_1 = 0$, $s_3 = -2k$, and the tangential stress $s_t = s_2 = 0$.

But the difficulty is to find the stress distribution in the ring described by the revolution of the plastic sector. This calculation seems
to be simple in annular co-ordinates, and the ball test is of such importance in engineering that we must check our assumptions.

On the element of the ring represented in section and in plan view in fig. 86, four forces act in the radial sense:

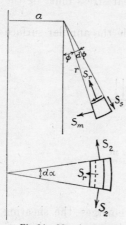

Fig. 86.—Notation for the computation of the stresses in the ring with quadrantal section in annular co-ordinates.

1. $\dfrac{\partial}{\partial r}\left\{s_r(a + r \sin\phi)\, d\alpha\, r\, d\phi\right\} dr,$

2. $\dfrac{\partial}{\partial \phi}\left\{s_s(a + r \sin\phi)\, d\alpha\, dr\right\} d\phi,$

3. $-s_m(a + r \sin\phi)\, d\alpha\, dr\, d\phi,$

4. $-s_2\, r\, d\phi\, dr\, d\alpha \sin\phi.$

And in the tangential direction four other forces act:

1. $\dfrac{\partial}{\partial \phi}\left\{s_m(a + r \sin\phi)\, d\alpha\, dr\right\} d\phi,$

2. $\dfrac{\partial}{\partial r}\left\{s_s(a + r \sin\phi)\, d\alpha\, r\, d\phi\right\} dr,$

3. $s_s(a + r \sin\phi)\, d\alpha\, dr\, d\phi,$

4. $-s_2\, r\, d\phi\, dr\, d\alpha \cos\phi.$

Equilibrium in the radial and tangential directions provides us with two differential equations:

$$\frac{\partial s_r}{\partial r}(ar + r^2 \sin\phi) + s_r(a + 2r \sin\phi) - s_m(a + r \sin\phi) + \frac{\partial s_s}{\partial \phi}(a + r\sin\phi)$$
$$+ s_s r \cos\phi - s_2 r \sin\phi = 0,$$
$$\frac{\partial s_m}{\partial \phi}(a + r \sin\phi) + s_m r \cos\phi + \frac{\partial s_s}{\partial r}(ar + r^2 \sin\phi)$$
$$+ s_s(2a + 3r \sin\phi) - s_2 \cos\phi = 0.$$

We also have available the condition of plasticity, but in general it is not possible to solve these equations. We can only test if the disposition of the lines of maximum shear stress, radii and circles, is exact (fig. 85).

Along these lines $s_s = k$ must fulfil all the conditions, and this will enable us to calculate s_m and s_r.

The stress circle shows that also $s_m = s_r = s_n$.

If what we have drawn is correct, then we have only to determine one unknown s_m as a function of r and ϕ. The tangential stress s_2 can be expressed in terms of s_m as $s_2 = s_m \pm k$, for we know from Chap. XIII that the mean principal stress must be equal to one of the other principal stresses. By these simplifications the differential equations become

$$\frac{\partial s_r}{\partial r} = -k \frac{\cos\phi \pm \sin\phi}{a + r\sin\phi}$$

and
$$\frac{\partial s_m}{\partial \phi} = -k \frac{2(a + r\sin\phi) \pm r\cos\phi + r\sin\phi}{a + r\sin\phi}.$$

The solutions are

$$s_r = -2k\phi - k \frac{\cos\phi \pm \sin\phi}{\sin\phi} \log_e \frac{a + r\sin\phi}{a} + C,$$

and
$$s_m = -2k\phi - k\left(\phi - \int \frac{d\phi}{1 + \frac{r}{a}\sin\phi}\right) \pm k \log_e \frac{a + r\sin\phi}{a} + C.$$

Now, if the assumed disposition of stresses were exact, then the expressions ought to be identical. Our test has shown that the lines of maximum shear stress must be situated otherwise. But some hope remains that the representation is an acceptable approximation.

At any rate, for $r = 0$, both expressions are identical as they ought to be, because at this point we must have the same expression as in the two-dimensional case. We simply find the expression of Hencky's law $s_r = s_m = -2k\phi + C$.

But we find everything in order also for $\phi = 0$, for the cylindrical section and for the horizontal tangential plane to the ring and

$$s_r = s_m = s_n = C.$$

For any other point of the ring the solution is wrong, as we find some difference between s_r and s_t, and this difference increases with r and ϕ. We now proceed to calculate this difference for the point where it is greatest, and in the first place we calculate s_r and s_m for the point $\phi = \frac{\pi}{4} = 45°$, $r = a\sqrt{2}$ and the sign $+$.

We start with the awkward integral

$$\int_0^{\pi/4} \frac{d\phi}{1 + \frac{r}{a}\sin\phi} = -\frac{1}{\sqrt{\left(\frac{r}{a}\right)^2 - 1}} \log_e \frac{\frac{r}{a} + \sin\phi + \sqrt{\left(\frac{r}{a}\right)^2 - 1}\cdot\cos\phi}{1 + \frac{r}{a}\sin\phi}\Bigg|_0^{\pi/4}$$

$$= -\frac{1}{\sqrt{\left(\frac{r}{a}\right)^2 - 1}} \log_e \frac{\frac{r}{a} + \frac{1}{2}\sqrt{2} + \frac{1}{2}\sqrt{2\left\{\left(\frac{r}{a}\right)^2 - 1\right\}}}{1 + \frac{1}{2}\frac{r}{a}\sqrt{2}}.$$

By this calculation we see that for the point where the difference between s_r and s_m is greatest

$$s_r = C - 2k\phi = C - 1{\cdot}571k.$$

$$s_m = C - 2k\phi - k\left(\frac{\pi}{4} - \log_e 2\right) + k\log_e\sqrt{2},$$

$$= C - 2k\phi - k\left(\frac{\pi}{4} - 2\log_e\sqrt{2}\right),$$

$$= C - 2k\phi - 0{\cdot}092k,$$

$$= C - 1{\cdot}571k - 0{\cdot}092k,$$

$$= C - 1{\cdot}663k.$$

We can find the integration constant C.

In the two-dimensional case $C = 0{\cdot}571k$, and as for $r = 0$ the stresses must be the same, the constant must also be the same.

We thus know that in fig. 85 where the divergence between s_r and s_m reaches a maximum we have $s_r = -k$, and $s_m = -1{\cdot}092k$, i.e. a discrepancy of 9 per cent, and that only for an unimportant corner of our figure.

We took s_2 equal to the smallest principal compressive stress $s_2 = s_m + k$ for the octant $\phi = 0$ to $\phi = 45°$. When we make the calculation for the other octant $\phi = 0$ to $\phi = -45°$, s_2 must be taken as $s_m - k$; that is to say, s_2 is equal to the maximum compressive stress. We then find for the most remote corner the same absolute difference between s_r and s_m, namely $0{\cdot}092k$, but here the fault is negligible because $s_r = -2{\cdot}571k$ and $s_m = -2{\cdot}479k$.

We must note the sudden jump of the tangential stress s_t from s_1 to s_3 when passing through $\phi = 0$, for which we have the cylinder of radius a. This curious behaviour becomes intelligible when we realize that at one side the material is compressed tangentially and at the other side it is stretched.

The reason for going through this long calculation is to show that the assumption of identical lines of maximum shearing stress as found in the two-dimensional problem is a reasonable approximation and that for plastic yield the pressure exerted by the ball is exactly

$$p = 2k(1 + 1{\cdot}571) = 2k \times 2{\cdot}571 = 2{\cdot}571s_0.$$

We must note that the pressure under a cylindrical punch just as under a ball, is equally distributed and as shown in fig. 87. The most interesting property of plastic flow is that a small displacement has no effect on the stress distribution. Even without calculation we might verify that the difference in pressure inside and outside the circle of radius a (fig. 86) is $p = 2 \cdot 57 s_0$. This is the correct formula for the ball test. In the zones corresponding to the triangular section, the

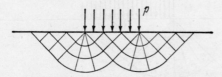

Fig. 87.—Shear-stress trajectories in plastic matter loaded by hydraulic pressure on a circular part of the surface

stresses cannot depart from the magnitude adopted at one point (fig. 87). And we know the difference at the circle d. We also know that the assumption of a circular quadrant as revolving area has failed, as we found some difference between s_r and s_m. To try to obtain a correct insight into the problem, we have recourse to experiment and measure the diameters of the indentation and of the dull circle made by a 10 mm. Brinell ball on the surface of polished test blocks by different loads.

Load in kg.	Diameter of indentation d in mm.	Diameter of dull spot D in mm.	D/d
1000	4·93	14	2·85
2000	5·6	15·2	2·72
3000	6·3	17·3	2·75
4000	6·9	18·9	2·74
5000	7·25	20	2·76
		Average	2·76

This is somewhat less than 3, as found for the two-dimensional problem.

2. The most instructive way for the engineer to account for the stress distribution in plastic flow is the graphical treatment. As there is no doubt as to the distribution in the parts with a triangular cross-

section, we restrict ourselves in fig. 88 to the treatment of the ring described by the revolution of the plastic sector for the case $d = 10$ cm., $D = 27 \cdot 6$ cm. This sector is not a quadrant of a circle but resembles a quadrant of an ellipse in which the curved radii normal to the curves are also drawn.

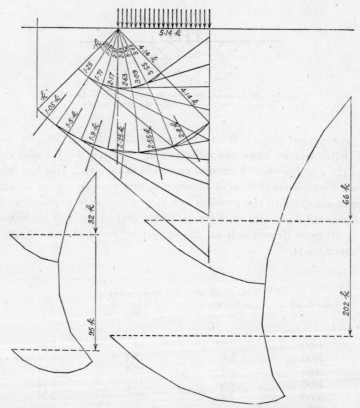

Fig. 88.—Graphical treatment of the yield-stress problem for a ball indentation

We approximate to the under-surface of the ring by six surfaces of truncated cones for which we calculate the normal force and the shearing force with the slide rule. Only the vertical components play a part. We add these forces using the polygon construction. The shearing stress along the trajectories is k everywhere.

Actual trial yielded the values shown in the figure. The resultant of all the forces is in equilibrium with the load $5 \cdot 14k = 2 \cdot 57s_0$ on the loaded circle, which gives a force of $202k$. There is also equilibrium of the solid of revolution obtained by cutting the plastified mass by the dotted cylinder. This is indicated in the figure, with $66k$ inscribed as the vertical force to the bottom surface, and $(202 - 66)k$ as the shearing force on the cylindrical surface. In the left-hand polygon the construction is repeated for the solid of revolution with about half the radius. We also tested other sections.

Anyone repeating the construction will find that the pressure on the bottom of the solid of revolution is less than in the case of the two-dimensional problem. There is no question of identity, but the important thing is that the main inference $p = 2\cdot57s_0$ as found by reasoning (and identical to the result of the two-dimensional problem) has been confirmed.

The horizontal components of the forces exerted on the outer surface of the plastic ring of quadrantal section, which might also be read in the polygon of forces, are left out. They are in equilibrium with the tangential forces $s_t = s_2$ which jump from s_1 to s_3 or adjust themselves automatically to ensure equilibrium. (See Chap. XIII, last paragraph.)

3. We must now explain why the yield point determined by this simple plastometer does not agree with the result found in a tensile test.

About thirty years ago, the publications on the Brinell test were numerous and extensive. We avail ourselves of the following results of indentation tests made by Mayer with great care.* The tensile test on the steel gave these figures:

Elongation 30 per cent measured on the length $l = 11\cdot3$ cm.
Reduction of area (A) 59 per cent.
Elastic limit under tension 26 kg./mm.²
Elastic limit under compression 31·5 kg./mm.²
Tensile strength 46·5 kg./mm.²

On examining the indentation and deformation, it is clear that this surpasses the limit to which the shear stress remains constant and equal to k.

In the ball test, work-hardening must be taken into account. In the tensile test with an area-reduction of $\psi = 59$ per cent, work-hardening goes to $\dfrac{100}{100-59} \times 46\cdot5 = 113$kg./mm.², and in a compression

* "Untersuchungen über Härteprüfung und Härte", *Zeitschr. des Vereines deutscher Ingenieure.* 25th April, 1908, pp. 646–8; *Forschungsarbeiten*, V. d. I. Heft, 65, 1909.

RESULTS OF INDENTATION TESTS WITH BALL OF 10 MM. DIAMETER

Load P on the ball in kg.	Diameter of the indentation d in mm.	Mean pressure $p = \dfrac{4P}{\pi d^2}$ in kg. per mm.^{2}	Yield point computed from formula $\dfrac{p}{2 \cdot 57}$ kg./mm.^{2}
520	2·317	123·0	48·0
800	2·829	127·3	49·5
1500	3·785	133·4	52·0
2000	4·285	138·5	54·0
2500	4·730	142·3	55·5

test (with which the ball test may be directly compared) it may go further. Fig. 89 shows the effect. As deformation to indentation surpasses the constant shear-stress limit, we understand that the figures in the last column are higher than the elastic limit of 31·5 kg./mm.^{2}, which for our purpose is the same as the yield limit.

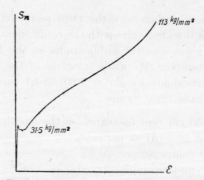

Fig. 89.—Resistance to plastic flow (s_n) as a function of the specific deformation ϵ for mild steel. In order to calculate s_n, the load is divided by the surface area of the deformed cross-section. The yield limit or hardness increases by work-hardening.

We would expect an increase in hardness with further deformation, and this is also confirmed. It is interesting to note and explain that an increase in hardness has no influence on the extent of the plastified zone, which remains limited to a diameter of 2·76 times the indentation.

The Brinell hardness is found by dividing the load P by the area of the segment of the sphere (which is, of course, greater than the

area of the projection of the segment). In this way, the work-hardening
is to some extent compensated and an empiric relation between Brinell
hardness and tensile strength may be given. This relation is distinct
for different materials.

4. Many tests have been made to investigate the behaviour of
indented metals.* The author made ball-hardness tests on clay. It
became clear that most experimenters used too small test blocks.
Sawn, polished and etched blocks of steel show a dark spot and a rootlike region under the indentation; and, in addition, both boundary
lines are at 45°. We see that the relief around the indentation is pre-
ceded by compression under the ball or by penetration of material in
the underlying layers until the resistance to elastic deformation exceeds
the pressure of $2 \cdot 57 s_0$. From fig. 85 it becomes clear that the thickness
of the test blocks must be at least $\frac{1}{2} d \sqrt{2}$.

On the photographs illustrating the publications* we can verify by
measurement that the diameter D of the plastic region is about $3d$,
and on the surface in plan view we see in the region $3d$ the logarithmic
spirals cutting circles and radii at angles of about 45°.

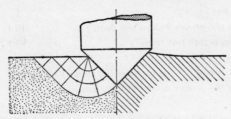

Fig. 90.—Cone indentation

5. Fig. 90 shows the cone hardness test. On the right we see the
relief of the crater-rim which is somewhat similar to that for the ball
test, at least when friction is sufficient.

Surface friction at the slightly lubricated point of the conical
punch is the questionable part of the cone test, but the friction of a
smooth punch seems to be sufficient to produce an indentation like
that of a perfectly rough punch. If this is so, it is all the same whether
the indentation is due to the point of the cone or to the cap of metal
adhering to the underside of the ball.

* G. Mesmer: " Vergleichende spannungsoptische Untersuchungen und Fliess-
versuche unter konzentrietem Druck," *Technische Mechanik und Thermodynamik*, Vol. I
(1930), No. 2, p. 85; Nadai, *Plasticity*, " Penetration of cylindrical punches ", pp. 235–8;
Hütte, 25th and 26th editions, *Mechanik der bildsamen Körper*.

CHAPTER XVI

The Grooved Cylindrical Test Bar

1. We now take up again the problem of fig. 34, Chap. V, and consider first an experimental investigation of the analogous three-dimensional case. Cylindrical test bars grooved and well annealed were submitted, some to a slight extension, others to a slight compression. Then they were sawn, heat-treated and etched to make the plastified regions visible. The result agreed fairly well with fig. 34. Fig. 91 is a drawing of a compression test piece. From the many samples examined, we reproduce as fig. 92 a photograph showing two etched test pieces of steel with a tensile strength after normalizing at 950° C. of 37 kg./mm.² and upper yield limit of 25 kg./mm.²

Number of test		1	2
Diameter in the groove before test (mm.)		10·1	10
Grooved area before test (mm.²)		80·1	78·5
Compressing load (kg.)		4000	7000
Compression stress on original area (kg./mm.²)		50	89·2
Diameter in the groove after the test (mm.)		10·4	11

Everybody will admit that in the first test (fig. 92, No. 1) the steel yielded over the whole area, and the plastic regions were fully developed. If, as in the ball test, we may assume the same formula as was deduced for the two-dimensional problem, then we have the following relation between compressive stress in the grooved cross-section and the yield limit at the moment of plastic flow through the whole area:

$$s_1 = (1 + \pi/4)s_0 = 1\cdot785 s_0.$$

We conclude from this formula that $s_0 = \dfrac{50}{1\cdot785} = 28$ kg./mm.² The yield limit was a little lower, viz. 25 kg./mm.², but the load of 4000 kg. was somewhat too high, as is shown by the increase in diameter. If this is taken into account, the result is in agreement with the formula.

On the etched cut of test piece No. 2 (fig. 92) two small black spots are visible indicating the original diameter. We draw the attention of the student to these points and invite him to reflect on the specific deformation (Chap. V, § 7). The groove is partly closed and work-hardening raised the yielding stress about 60 per cent. If he is reluctant to acknowledge the demonstrative power of etchings with such stripes and feathers, he must study the illustrated articles of Nadai.* For the analogous two-dimensional problem, where the same formula $p = s_0(1 + \pi/4)$ is generally accepted, the photographs are no better.

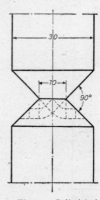

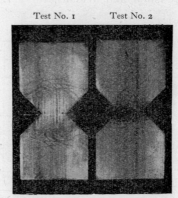

Test No. 1   Test No. 2

Fig. 91.—Cylindrical compression test piece, circularly grooved.

Fig. 92.—Test pieces of fig. 91 loaded with 4000 kg. (left) and 7000 kg. (right)

Another confirmation of the validity of fig. 91 for solids of revolution may be obtained by studying figs. 64, 65 and 66 in Nadai's publication. They show truncated cones of paraffin pressed into each other at the points.

2. Much information has been published on grooved round bars. We start with the best confirmation of our theory that we know.

A series of tests on a ductile aluminium alloy, called Lautal, was carried out, and the yield stress s_0 determined.† According to our assumption the same formula must be applied as in the two-dimensional case, i.e. $p = (1 + \phi)s_0$, in which ϕ represents the angle of the plastic sector. p is a linear function of ϕ, and we can draw the line be-

* *Zeitschrift für technische Physik*, 1924, p. 1369, &c., " Ueber die unter einer Belastung sich bildenden Gleitflächen der festen Körper ".

† " Mitteilungen der deutschen Materialprüfungsanstalten ", *Sonderheft*, XX, 1932, Kohäsionsfestigkeit.

cause we know that for $\phi = 0$, we have the yield stress of a cylindrical bar, and for $\phi = 90° = \dfrac{\pi}{2}$ radians, $p = 2 \cdot 57 s_0$, the yield stress of a sharp incision such as a round hair crack. We can draw the line if only we know the ordinary tensile yield stress.

The results of the experiments are shown in fig. 93, where the yield stress is given as a function of the angle of the groove (the supplement of twice the angle ϕ).

Another important investigation on this subject has been carried out by Thum and Wunderlich.* In order to prevent their results

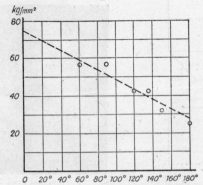

Fig. 93.—Apparent yield limit as a function of the
groove angle for the light alloy Lautal

being used to dispute our theory we must discuss their experiment. They wrote, "The grooved area flows at all points when $s_n = 35 \cdot 2$ kg./mm.² (tensile test on straight bars, upper yield stress $28 \cdot 5$ kg./mm.², lower yield stress $23 \cdot 9$ kg./mm.², tensile strength $34 \cdot 3$ kg./mm.²)."

Calculated with our formula the grooved bar would have flowed at

$$s_n = (1 + \pi/4)s_0 = 1 \cdot 785 s_0.$$

The experiment has given

$$s_n = \frac{35 \cdot 2}{23 \cdot 9} s_0 = 1 \cdot 475 s_0$$

if the lower yield point is taken into account, as we think it must.

The bar flowed earlier than according to theory. But if we compare the test piece examined under compression by Thum and Wunderlich,

* *Forchung*, Band 3 (1932), p. 267, "5. Das Fliessen bei gekerbten Rundstäben".

as drawn in fig. 94, with ours shown in fig. 91, we see that the plastic region as assumed by us could not develop completely owing to the lack of depth of the groove. In the grooved area we want a tension of $1 \cdot 785 s_0$. The shaft flows at a tension s_0. If the diameter is not reduced to less than 75 per cent, the shaft has a greater resistance to through-yielding than the grooved section. Although a nice square becomes visible on the etched meridian section, we cannot expect agreement with our formula. The discrepancy is instructive.

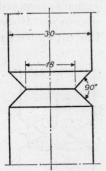

3. It would take too much space to discuss fully the elaborate publication on grooved bars by W. Kuntze, to which we have several objections.* We only point to one property of solid matter of which Kuntze was unaware, although it influences his results considerably.

In a tensile test we have not only to overcome the yield stress but also the surface tension, which for ordinary mild steel is about 16 kg./mm. We refer to figs. 12 and 13 of Kuntze, where he was very near discovering this effect; but he did not draw the conclusion.†

Fig. 94.—Test bar, with groove depth insufficient for complete plastification of reduced cross-section.

Yet from these his own experiments, we see that tests with bars grooved to less than 8 mm. diameter are unreliable. Kuntze went to about 2 mm., and by extrapolating on these erroneous results, he built his theory.

Just as with the experiments of Thum and Wunderlich who worked with bars grooved to insufficient depth, no agreement with our formula is obtained when the bars are grooved too deeply. But when both extremes are excluded, the mass of experimental material procured by Kuntze provides a striking confirmation of the formula $p = s_0(1 + \phi)$.

To show this we give another of Kuntze's tests ‡ taken under good

* *Kohäsionsfestigkeit*, 1932.

† *Lueger Lexikon der gesamten Technik*, III, p. 16. Tensile strength of annealed iron wire, $k_2 = 28 \cdot 7 + \dfrac{64}{d}$ kg./mm.² Hence surface tension, $\gamma = \dfrac{64}{4} = 16$ kg./mm. The general formula for the tensile strength of wires is $k_2 = k_0 + \dfrac{c}{d}$. It follows from both figures of Kuntze, $\gamma = 18 \cdot 7$ and $\gamma = 14 \cdot 3$. Mean value, $16 \cdot 5$ kg./mm.

‡ " Einfluss ungleichförmig verteilter Spannungen auf die Festigkeit von Werkstoffen " (*Aus dem staatlichen Materialprüfungsamt Berlin-Dahlem. Maschinenelemente Tagung*, Achen, 1936).

conditions. One of the test bars is drawn in fig. 95. In the description of the test, we read:

Lower yield stress, 18·8 kg./mm.²

Upper yield stress, 23 kg./mm.²

The bar began to lengthen when the mean tension in the grooved section approached the yield stress. At 42·2 kg./mm.² yield became so obvious that it was clear that plastic flow occurred all over the section. The bar broke at 50 kg./mm.² If we take the mean yield stress

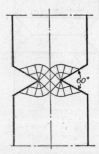

$\dfrac{18 \cdot 8 + 23}{2} = 20 \cdot 5$ kg./mm.², flow over the whole section should occur when $p = s_0(1 + \pi/3) = 2 \cdot 056 s_0 = 42 \cdot 2$ kg./mm.² in perfect agreement with experiment.

In Chap. XXIII we shall show that the small curvature of the bottom of the groove has no influence.

At the State Mines, too, we made many experiments to investigate the etchings at different stages of elongation. With round bars of 22 mm. diameter, incised by a rectangular groove to a diameter of 10 mm., the inner square became just

Fig. 95. — Grooved cylindrical test bar used by Kuntze.

visible on the etchings when the mean tension at the reduced diameter was 40·6 kg./mm.² The upper yield stress, the mean of two tests, was 30·1 kg./mm.², so that it has been proved that indications of plastification become visible long before the whole area plastifies. Even at a load of 48·8 kg./mm.² in the critical section plastic flow did not occur throughout. But this was certainly the case at 57·6 kg./mm.² The theoretical calculation gives

$$s_1 = s_0(1 + \phi) = 1 \cdot 705 s_0 = 1 \cdot 705 \times 30 \cdot 1 = 53 \cdot 7 \text{ kg./mm.}^2$$

The numerous experiments described in Chap. XX, § 2, also confirm the applicability of this formula.

4. The fact that the stresses in the central double cone (fig. 95) under plastic flow can be calculated by the above formula (the same as for the two-dimensional case) is not only proved by experiment but may also be checked by the reasoning used for the ball and for the punch indentation. But no more can be asserted than that at corresponding points of the solid of revolution and of the strip of the same cross-section the stresses are the same. This holds true near the bottom of the groove and in the double cone. The stress distribution in the other zones of the plastified region can best be determined by a semi-graphical method.

In fig. 96 are drawn on a large scale the trajectories of maximum shear stress. At the periphery of the plastic region is marked the normal stress where this can be calculated. Along the plastic sector we draw to scale the normal pressure, which is obtained by trying values until vertical equilibrium is assured not only for the whole plastic ring but also for the parts of it.

That the section of the plastic ring with curved trajectories is an octant may be considered as a fact sanctioned by experiment.

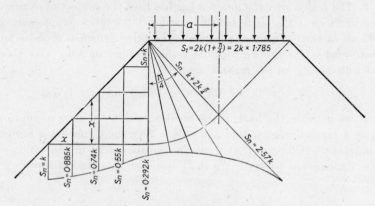

Fig. 96.—Stress distribution in a grooved tensile test bar at the moment of plastic flow on the entire reduced cross-section

For the plastic sector with a small tip angle, the circle as boundary line is quite in order. If the angle approaches 90°, we arrive at the elliptical curve dealt with in the preceding chapter whose axes differ by about 8 per cent. In our case the difference is only a few per cent, too small to be taken into account in the drawing. It follows from a simple integration that the normal pressure under the base of the ring described by the isosceles rectangular triangle in fig. 96 is expressed by

$$s_n = \frac{a + a\sqrt{2} - 2x}{a + a\sqrt{2} - x}\, k,$$

in which k represents the yield shearing stress and a and x are indicated in the figure. Equilibrium in the tangential direction is assured by the peculiarity of s_2 to adapt itself to circumstances. s_2 can jump in adjacent fibres from s_1 to s_3. Generally speaking, $s_2 = s_n \pm k$. It is easy to prove that the mean value of s_2 lies between these two extremes. But instead of imagining this stress to jump backward and forward we may think of it adjusting itself according to circumstances and remaining between these extreme values, so that the theorem of Coulomb-Guest holds.

In the central cone the principal stresses are everywhere

$$s_1 = -1.57k, \quad s_2 = -1.57k, \quad s_3 = -3.57k$$

under the assumption that we are dealing with pressure.

5. The reason why the grooved bar has been the subject of so many investigations is that it is rightly considered the most comprehensive instance of three-dimensional stress. The three principal stresses are greatest when the groove becomes a sharp round incision. We then find with tension in the central cone,

$$s_1 = s_0(1 + \pi/2) = 2.57s_0, \quad s_2 = 1.57s_0 \text{ and } s_3 = 1.57s_0.$$

If we increase the load to the breaking-point, the area of rupture shows a crystalline structure and only a very small rim has a fibrous appearance. If follows that a brittle rupture occurs in the region of three-dimensional tension. We shall deal with this kind of rupture in Chap. XX.

CHAPTER XVII

Plastic Torsion

1. The best book on this subject is *Plasticity*, by Nadai.* We refer to this famous textbook for the masterly treatment of stress-distribution in bars of different section, subjected to torsional over-strain. It contains much useful information and experimental data and may be strongly recommended. The reader will soon detect, however, that our conception of plastic flow is at a variance with that of Nadai, but as to the chapters on plastic torsion we can only recognize his classical treatment.†

In order to make this book complete we include a concise account of torsional stress in ductile matter and start with the simplest case— the cylindrical bar subjected to pure torsion. The yield shear stress is first reached at the circumference, and when the torque is increased the annular region of plastic flow spreads to the interior.

It is generally accepted that in this region of plastic flow, the three principal stresses are $s_1 = k$, $s_2 = 0$ and $s_3 = -k$. In Chap. XXIII, § 11, we shall see that, although this is not exact, the stress differences and the shearing stresses are correct. With these principal stresses we should have $s_s = s_0/\sqrt{3}$, but an imposing amount of experimental data proves that $s_s = k = s_0/2$. It is also a question as to whether the material flows according to the hypothesis of Huber-Hencky or to that of Coulomb-Guest, or whether both hypotheses accord. At any rate (and this is important) *the shearing stress is constant in the region of plastic flow.*

Let R denote the radius of the cylindrical bar and r_e the radius of the circle delimiting the regions of elastic and plastic deformation. Then the torque is $T = \dfrac{\pi k}{3}\left(2R^3 - \dfrac{r_e^3}{2}\right)$, which the reader may readily verify. Following Prandtl, the torsional stresses in a bar may be represented by a heap or hill erected on the section of the bar. The

---

* McGraw-Hill Book Company, New York and London, 1931.

† The well-illustrated article of Bader and Nadai: " Die Vorgänge nach Ueberschreitung der Fliessgrenze in verdrehten Eisenstäben", *Zeitschr. der Ver. deutsch, Ingenieure*, **71** (1927), pp. 317–23.

slope, taken to an appropriate scale, is a measure of the torsional or shearing stress. This analogy is based on the following argument:

The axial equilibrium of an element $dx\,dy$ of unit length, subjected to torsional stress s_s with components s_x and s_y, gives

$$\frac{\partial s_x}{\partial x} + \frac{\partial s_y}{\partial y} = 0,$$

because the shearing stresses in the axial sense are likewise s_x and s_y. Now this expression is equivalent to the simultaneous expressions

$$s_x = \frac{\partial h}{\partial y} \quad \text{and} \quad s_y = -\frac{\partial h}{\partial x},$$

where h, a function of x and y, is the height of the heap. This holds true for the case of elastic as well as for plastic deformation. For elastic torsion the surface of the heap is analogous to a soap-film or an elastic membrane placed over the circumference of the bar slightly inflated. For plastic torsion the heap has the shape of a roof with equal slope to the circumference, erected over the section because

$$s_s = \sqrt{s_x{}^2 + s_y{}^2} = k.$$

This shearing stress is parallel to the circumference, but the lines of maximum slope representing the torsional stress are in projection perpendicular to the torsional stress. So are also their components

$$\frac{\partial h}{\partial x} = -s_y \quad \text{and} \quad \frac{\partial h}{\partial y} = s_x.$$

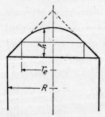

Fig. 97.—The torsional stress heap for a cylindrical bar twisted to yield over the annular part of the cross-section between R and r_e.

Rain-water flows along the lines of steepest slope of the hill.

If the contour of the cross-section is cut out of stiff paper, or if the bar itself is placed with the cross-section horizontal and covered with as much dry sand as it can carry, there results a heap whose natural slope at any point represents the torsional stress in overstrain. Its form is independent of the amount of twist.

In fig. 97 the torsional stress heap is shown for the twisted cylindrical bar. Up to the delimiting circle with radius r_e between plastic and elastic torsion the slope is constant. In the elastic zone the heap is a paraboloid. The slope, indicating the tangential or torsional shearing stress in the centre, is, of course, zero.

2. What is the distribution of torsional stress in a bar of rectangular cross-section, having sides $2a$ and $2b$ (fig. 98) when twisted to the completely plastic state?

In the section four zones may be distinguished in each of which the shear stress $s_s = k$ is parallel to a side of the rectangle. The calculation of the torque gives

$$T = (4ab^2 - \tfrac{4}{3}b^3)k.$$

3. In fig. 99 we have shown a roof with constant slope to the edge having an elliptical cross-section. This form of roof is obtained by pouring fine dry sand on the elliptic section. The horizontal projections of the lines of constant slope are the normals to the ellipse.

The sand heap on a cross-section which is a regular polygon is a pyramid.

For the cross-section of a shaft with a semicircular keyway a cone is obtained from which a part is cut away by another cone.

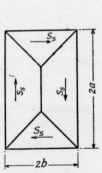

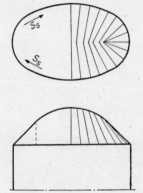

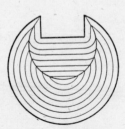

Fig. 98.—Shear-stress roof with constant slope, representing the stress function for complete plastic yield in a bar with rectangular cross-section.

Fig. 99.—The construction of a roof with constant slope above an elliptical cross-section. The normals to the circumference bisect the angles between the lines to the foci.

Fig. 100.—Lines of equal level of a sand heap on the cross-section of a shaft with a keyway.

4. In fig. 100 we show, in plan, the sand heap representing the torsional stress-function for the cross-section of a shaft with a square keyway.

The heap is represented by the horizontal lines or contours around the surface of the heap at equidistant levels, as in a geodetic survey.

The strength of the shaft under plastic torsion is much reduced by the keyway, but this is insignificant compared to the weakening under elastic stress distribution. The membrane analogy shows an infinite stress at the sharp corners of the keyway in this case as at the vertices of the re-entrant angles the inflated membrane rises vertically.

The plasticity of matter limits the torsional stress to the yield shear stress.

An extension of the sand-heap analogy for perfect plastic torsion of sections with one or more openings is given by M. A. Sadowski.*

* *Journal of Applied Mechanics, Trans. A.S.M.E.*, Vol. 63, Dec. 1941, p. A. 166.

CHAPTER XVIII

Do Slip Planes Occur in Plastic Flow?

1. In order to improve our understanding of plastic flow a chapter must be devoted to the relative displacement of the particles in matter strained beyond the elastic limit. Let us imagine a test block uniformly compressed between perfectly lubricated endplanes. The greatest shear stress occurs on all planes which make an angle of 45° with the axis. When the elastic limit is passed and all the elements shorten and widen, there can be no question of slip planes. Particles in one horizontal layer penetrate an underlying layer. Many particles get new neighbours. Ranks may be doubled.

In the plastic state the material resembles a liquid, with this difference, that in a liquid the three principal stresses are alike, and in solid matter they may be all different. For plastic flow the mean principal stress becomes equal to one of the extremes (Chap. XIII), and then the similarity to a liquid becomes obvious. The material flows to the sides of less resistance and any conception of slip planes is misleading.

In order to assist the reader to form a picture of what happens in plastic flow, we give here the simplest scheme for the displacement of the particles when the mass is compressed to two-thirds of its original thickness. The particles are indicated by the letters of the alphabet.

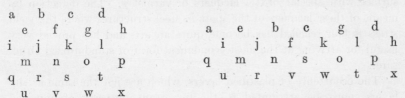

Before compression   After compression to two-thirds
                                         of the original thickness

We have made particles of the second and fifth layers move into the layers situated above and below. The particles move in space without any regularity. Even whole lumps may intrude between other masses of the material. But one thing is certain—slip planes do not occur.

And yet, when a test piece of mild steel is compressed, or suffers any other slight deformation, the belief in slip planes is reinforced by observation. Fig. 101 shows a few lines marking the so-called slip planes on two sides of a square test piece. The figure is drawn from a good photograph.*

These quasi-slip planes manifest themselves in the following way:

1. On the polished surfaces of mild steel or annealed iron, dull lines appear when the yield stress is reached, indicating planes coinciding approximately with the planes of maximum shear stress. But seldom are the observers aware of the real difference. Often angles of 72° and 108° are seen between the planes as indicated in fig. 101, while the planes of maximum shearing stress make angles of 90°.†

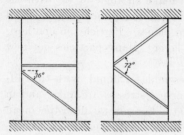

Fig. 101.—Lines indicating plastic layers observed on the sides of a test block of mild steel.

2. By etching with Fry's liquor (copper chloride in hydrochloric acid) after heat treatment of the polished sections of slightly bent or strained test pieces of mild steel, lines and regions of deformation become visible, which are often interpreted as slip lines.

3. When test pieces or steel structural parts have been annealed in air or are covered with a coating of rust or scale before being deformed beyond the elastic limit, the scale flakes off along the lines where the so-called slip planes intersect the surface. This looks very impressive.

4. In a similar way these lines can be made visible by covering the surface with special brittle lacquers or varnishes. The detection by means of these lacquers of the spots in steel structures where the yield stress is first reached has become quite an art, and has proved very useful for arriving at the most economical form of standardized structure.

The occurrence of plastified layers, which are not the same as slip layers, must be attributed to the important property of annealed

---

* Fig. 34, *Handbuch der Physik*, VI, pp. 458–9. Compare also figs. 30–36, or Hütte, I, 25th or 26th Edition, p. 342, Slip lines or Lüders lines. Fine pictures may be found in Nadai, *Plasticity*, pp. 86–119.

† In France the lines which become visible on the polished surface of mild steel when the limit of plasticity is reached are called " Hartmann lines " after the famous publication of an artillery officer: *Distribution des déformations dans les métaux soumis à des efforts*, Paris, 1896. This is recommended. In Nadai, *Plasticity*, p. 86, and in *Lexikon der gesamten Technik*, IV, p. 91, many references are given.

mild steel, that the yield limit suddenly drops when plastic deformation of the steel starts. Although this explanation is not very convincing, we get a good idea of what happens at that moment if we imagine
that the ferrite crystals are cemented by strong but brittle ferrous oxide
or by a skeleton of cementite. When this rigid skeleton breaks down
at the higher yield point, the ferrite crystals are free to deform plastically, and the yield point drops by the amount shown in figs. 4 and 89.

If the reader is convinced that a drop in resistance occurs when the
elastic limit is passed, then he must accept the presence of plastic layers.

At the spot where the skeleton first breaks down (similarly to what
occurs at the end of a crack) we have to deal with a concentration of
stresses and a plastified layer jumps through the test piece, being made
visible by a fall in the autographic tensile diagram. But no slip occurs.
In the plastic layer the atoms of the ferrite crystals rearrange themselves. As soon as the material is strengthened by cold-working, the
elongation or compression in this layer stops and another layer is plastified. A net of Lüder or Hartmann lines appears
on the surface and becomes denser with further
deformation. When all the material is reinforced,
neither Fry's liquor nor any varnish will produce
a line network. The etching shows a dark region
and the polished surface becomes evenly dull.

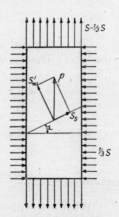

2. We are now confronted with the problem:
how are these thin layers along which plastification originates orientated with respect to the
principal directions? At first it is tempting to
suppose that they are in accord with the planes
of maximum shear stress, especially if we believe
in slip planes. But these planes do not exist,
and, moreover, the inclination of 45° to the main

Fig. 102—Plastic layers
in a tensile bar

principal stress is not confirmed by observation.

We start with the calculation for the simplest case, that of the
angle α between the plastified layer and the cross-section of a bar in
tension or compression as shown in fig. 102. The basis of our calculation is that plastification depends only on shear stress. To eliminate
all influence of change in volume, we superpose a general pressure $-s/3$
on the test bar. We then deal with the principal stresses

$$s_1' = \frac{2}{3}\,s, \quad s_2' = -\frac{s}{3} \quad \text{and} \quad s_3' = -\frac{s}{3}.$$

At every point of the layer indicated in fig. 102 occur the tensions

$$s_{n1}' = \frac{s_1' + s_2'}{2} + \frac{s_1' - s_2'}{2} \cos 2\alpha = \frac{s}{2}(\tfrac{1}{3} + \cos 2\alpha) = s(\cos^2\alpha - \tfrac{1}{3}),$$

$$s_{n2}' = \frac{s_1' + s_2'}{2} - \frac{s_1' - s_2'}{2} \cos 2\alpha = \frac{s}{2}(\tfrac{1}{3} - \cos 2\alpha) = s(\tfrac{2}{3} - \cos^2\alpha),$$

$$s_s = \frac{s_1' - s_2'}{2} \sin 2\alpha = \frac{s}{2} \sin 2\alpha = s \cos\alpha \sin\alpha.$$

The reader is invited to check these expressions by drawing the stress circle for pure tension.

By the accents in s_{n1}', s_{n2}', &c., we indicate that we consider the distortion only, and have eliminated the change of volume which, moreover, may be supposed to be the same for the substance in both the elastic and plastic states. This we leave aside for the moment.

The following conditions are fulfilled:

$$s_1' + s_2' + s_3' = 0, \quad s_{n1}' + s_{n2}' + s_3' = 0, \quad s_{n1}' + s_3' = -s_{n2}'.$$

Let us now calculate the specific elongation ϵ_2' in the direction of the layer. The whole calculation is made for this purpose. The elongation is

$$\epsilon_2' = \frac{s_{n2}'}{E} - \frac{s_{n1}' + s_3'}{mE} = \frac{s_{n2}'}{E} + \frac{s_{n2}'}{mE} = \frac{s}{2G}(\tfrac{2}{3} - \cos^2\alpha).$$

When $\cos^2\alpha = \tfrac{2}{3}, \quad \alpha = 35° \, 15' \, 52'',$

or $\cos 2\alpha = \tfrac{1}{3}, \quad 2\alpha = 70° \, 31' \, 44'',$

then $\epsilon_2' = 0.$

What is the physical meaning of $\epsilon_2' = 0$? In general, a thin plastic layer compressed or drawn between parallel planes, with or without a tangential force, will exert an enormous resistance as soon as it begins to move (fig. 42). We have studied this effect in Chap. VI. But here the situation is quite different. We found the exceptional layer for which the plastic substance does not expand, and we not only note this fact, but also by calculating s_{n2}' see that the stress in the direction of this layer ($\alpha = 35° \, 15' \, 52''$) is zero.

But we may ask in which direction the material is pushed, and whence is it drawn, when the test piece is loaded in compression or in tension. Of course the answer is: in the direction of s_3'; and, indeed, as Hartmann has already observed, we detect at the sides of the test piece a low ridge in the case of compression and a shallow groove in the case of tension. If we touch the polished surfaces with sandpaper when the test pieces have previously been annealed so as to obtain a blue colour, we find in these slight extrusions or intrusions the best way of detecting the Hartmann lines. The method is due to Hartmann.

It is easy to imagine by a glance at fig. 42 that plastification in a layer ceases as soon as it has started. There is no great preference for the layers at $54° \ 44' \ 8''$ with the axis to be plastified, but at any rate plasticity does occur somewhat more easily in these than in other layers.

Although of minor importance, we calculate $s_{n1}' = s/3$. This is half the value of s_1' and

$$\epsilon_1' = \frac{s_{n1}'}{2G} = \frac{s}{6G}.$$

Of somewhat more importance may be the remark that the sudden change in m, E and G, which occurs at the moment of plastification, does not influence our calculation, nor our conclusion. The plastified layer fits in, only now at an inclination of about $35°$. In all other layers the substance in plastic flow would grip by the difference in E and G as soon as it was set in motion. In our extraordinary layer and above and below it $\epsilon_n' = 0$ whatever E and G might be.

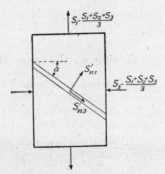

Fig. 103.—The inclination of Hartmann or Lüders lines in mild steel subjected to three-dimensional stress to the upper yield point.

3. We now proceed with the general case and calculate the inclination of the Hartmann lines, or more properly expressed, the inclination of the layers of incipient plastification when we have to deal with three different principal stresses s_1, s_2 and s_3.

This case is represented by fig. 103. For reasons of symmetry we can imagine that plastic layers must occur as conjugate planes perpendicular to the plane s_1, s_3, but it is probable that α is a function of s_1, s_2 and s_3. We superpose $- \dfrac{s_1 + s_2 + s_3}{3}$ and deal with

$$s_1' = \frac{2}{3}s_1 - \frac{s_2}{3} - \frac{s_3}{3}, \quad s_3' = -\frac{s_1}{3} - \frac{s_2}{3} + \frac{2}{3}s_3.$$

In Mohr's circle we see that the stress s_{n2}' in the direction of the layer at the angle α with the plane s_2, s_3 and normal to the plane s_1, s_2 is

$$s_{n2}' = \frac{s_1' + s_3'}{2} - \frac{s_1' - s_3'}{2} \cos 2\alpha$$

$$= \frac{s_1 + s_3}{6} - \frac{s_2}{3} - \frac{s_1 - s_3}{2} \cos 2\alpha.$$

For the layer orientated at such an angle that $s_{n2}' = 0$ and $\epsilon_2' = 0$ we find

$$\cos 2\alpha = \tfrac{1}{3} \cdot \frac{s_1 + s_3 - 2s_2}{s_1 - s_3}.$$

If $s_2 = 0$, $s_3 = 0$, $s_1 = s$, we have the expression for the case dealt with in § 2. We shall now prove that this value ($\cos 2\alpha = \tfrac{1}{3}$, $\alpha = 35°\ 16'$) is the greatest possible deviation that plastic layers can show from the planes of maximum shear stress for which the angle is 45°. We ask: what is the least value of α, or the greatest for $\cos 2\alpha$?

To show that α depends only on stress differences we write

$$\cos 2\alpha = \tfrac{1}{3} \frac{(s_1 - s_2) - (s_2 - s_3)}{s_1 - s_3}.$$

Varying s_2, the numerator of the fraction becomes as great as possible when $s_2 = 0$, and then $\cos 2\alpha = \tfrac{1}{3} \cdot \frac{s_1 + s_3}{s_1 - s_3}$. When s_2 is zero, s_3, the smallest principal stress, is negative. In general, it is only the difference of the principal stresses which matters. The maximum of $\cos 2\alpha$ occurs when $s_2 = s_3$. If, then, $s_3 = 0$ the greatest value of $\cos 2\alpha = \tfrac{1}{3}$. Thus $\alpha = 35°\ 16'$ is the minimum inclination.

4. And what is the greatest inclination the layer can reach? α becomes a maximum when the numerator of the fraction is zero, i.e. $s_1 + s_3 = 2s_2$. The mean principal stress must just be the mean of the extreme stresses.

In this case alone, for instance under pure shear or torsion, the layers in which plastification starts, with which the workers in plasticity are so much concerned, coincide with the planes of maximum shearing stress. In all other cases the angle between the Hartmann lines may vary from 70° 31' to 90°. In fig. 104 we give a construction for the extreme values of α. No wonder that it was long before proper attention was paid to the difference. It is to the credit of Professor

P. P. Bylaard at Bandoeng * that attention was drawn to this phenomenon. He has confirmed the formula for α by well-chosen tests.

As the angle between conjugate plastic layers depends on the stress
differences, we can draw conclusions as to these stresses when we
measure the angle. On the first photograph (fig. 49), *Handbuch der
Physik*, VI, p. 474 (Plasticity), we find for the angles between the sets
of spirals surrounding the *deep* indentation of a punch in mild steel,
values decreasing from 90° for the diameter d to 71° 30' for the diameter $3d$. From this we may deduce that at the boundary of the plastified zone the principal stresses were $s_1 = s_0$, $s_2 = 0$ and $s_3 = 0$, and at
the inner circle where the punch made a deep indentation $s_1 = s_0/2$,
$s_2 = 0$ and $s_3 = -s_0/2$.

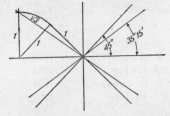

Fig. 104.—Greatest deviation between maximum
shear stress and plastified layers.   A construction
for the angle of 35° is given at the left.

We repeat that the occurrence of plastified layers is due to a drop
in the yield stress. Work-hardening stops their development. But
before disruption, when the total tension falls, a similar phenomenon
becomes apparent. This only ceases at the moment of breakdown
when it shows at the surfaces of fibrous rupture, the angles we should
expect from our formula. Indeed, in an actual measurement the inclination of the indentation of a broken tensile strip to the normal
cross-section was found to be about 36°. For the angle between the
wall of cone and cup and the outside surface of a broken round test
bar, we found an average value of just 54° (fig. 108). Angles of 35°
and 55° are met with in practice for Hartmann lines and angles of
rupture, because often two principal stresses are equal. Then the
formula for the tensile bar gives $\cos 2\alpha = \frac{1}{3}$, $\alpha = 35°$, and for the steel
sheet evenly stressed in its plane as $s_1 = s_2 = s$, $s_3 = 0$, we obtain
$\alpha = 55°$, which also means an angle of 35° with the surfaces.

* *De Ingenieur*, 1931, p. B. 249, and 1933, p. B. 129.   One also may study the remarkable application of this relation; F. A. Vening Meinesz, " Stresses in the Earth's
crust in consequence of polar displacements ", *Académie Néerlandaise des Sciences*,
Vol III, No. 5, 1943, p. 185.

9

5. When in the examination of stress-strain phenomena we meet with occurrences for which at first sight we see no explanation, we must have recourse to the theory of plasticity. Much controversy has taken place because many authors found a higher limit of elasticity or yield point in bending tests than in tensile tests with bars of square cross-section of the same mild steel.* The key to the solution of this mysterious contradiction is found when we know that the phenomenon is most marked for these materials which show the greatest drop from upper to lower yield point.

Different experimenters have found these results:

Authors	Year	Difference in yield point found by bending and tensile tests (per cent)
A. Thum and F. Wunderlich	1932	35 to 45
H. Möller and J. Barbers	1934	40
E. Siebel and F. H. Vieregge	1934	28
H. Möller and J. Barbers	1935	13
F. Rinagl	1936	0
F. Bollenrath and J. Schmied	1938	0

The more precisely the first indication of plastic yield could be observed, the smaller the difference became. When we adhere to the conception that the crystallites are cemented together by a strong but brittle skeleton, the phenomenon is explained. In the tensile test we have a sudden drop in stress when the upper yield stress is reached, because the skeleton, equally strained, breaks throughout. In the bending test, the skeleton only breaks at the surface. As it is less strained in the deeper regions it resists fracture there. We see from etchings of polished sections that plastified layers occur throughout the tensile bar. In bending tests, however, short black lines start at regular intervals from the surface and very soon die out.

* A documentated study on this subject is found in *Zeitschr. der Ver. deutscher Ingenieure*, 1938, p. 1094, in an article by Bollenrath and Schmied.

More recently an important study of this subject with a list of literature has been published by F. K. G. Odguist and C. Schaub of the Royal Technical Institute of Sweden at Stockholm (1947).

CHAPTER XIX

The Strengthening of Mild Steel by Work-hardening

1. The theory of plasticity is based on Coulomb's assumption according to which the maximum shear stress is constant during plastic flow. In later years experiments have shown that plastic yield sets in when the shearing stress on the octahedral planes reaches $s_{sc} = \frac{1}{3}s_0\sqrt{2}$, in which s_0 is the upper yield limit. But we have seen in the former chapter that for a small deformation, when the skeleton cementing the ferrite crystals is ruptured, the yield limit drops below this value of s_{sc}. And now we shall deal with another property of mild steel which becomes prominent when the deformation is pushed so far that the steel becomes reinforced. The reinforcement by cold-working may be very important. Work-hardening, moreover, makes the steel somewhat brittle. If the hypothesis of Coulomb holds till rupture occurs, the steel ought to be stretched like syrup or heated glass, and, when we leave surface tension out of consideration, the pull should decrease in inverse proportion to the extension. In fact, the pull in a tensile test increases until the tensile strength is reached. The true stress at the cross-section where necking occurs and work-hardening is most pronounced, may even reach three times the yield stress. Application of the law that maximum shear stress $= k$ at plastic flow in materials subjected to work-hardening would be erroneous.

Physicists have found by tensile tests on bars consisting of a single crystal, that the strengthening depends on the magnitude of the sliding of the lamellae in the crystal. For this reason the reinforcement of steel is the same, whether the deformation is obtained by extension, compression or by a combination of these forms of strain. But we are of opinion that when extended, the material subject to plastic flow breaks more easily in consequence of internal rupture occurring over flaws (compare Chap. XXII).

A mathematical treatment of the breakdown during plastic flow beyond the strain at which work-hardening sets in, implies the formulation of the law relating reinforcement to deformation. This is not the law expressed by fig. 5 of § 3, Chap. I. We now deal with the ultimate true tensile stress which can be obtained by cold-working. In the next chapter we shall see that this stress has a real physical meaning although the cone-and-cup rupture shows two different zones.

In 1944, under the supervision of W. J. D. Fokkinga, a series of accurate tensile tests was made at the author's request in the metallographic laboratories of the State Mines, on similar cylindrical test bars of different length and diameter. The bars were of the same material normalized at 900° C. for 20 minutes, and then slightly polished. The steel was very even in composition, but somewhat hard. The average tensile strength was 43·3 kg./mm.²; lower yield limit 28·5 kg./mm.²; extension for $l = 5d$, average 32·5 per cent.

It is well known, and confirmed by these experiments, that the tensile strength of bars of different size is the same, unless we go to bars of a few mm. diameter, in which case the superficial tension becomes appreciable. But it was a revelation that a very marked influence of size of test bar on contraction and true breaking strength could be detected. The tensile strength, calculated on the original cross-section, depends only on the load at which necking of the bar begins. There is no question of work-hardening until we have a good deal of necking.

If we call the original cross-section A_1, and the neck section A_2, the maximum load on the test bar, i.e. the load on incipient necking, P and the load at the moment of rupture P_e, then we have the following definitions:

$$R = P/A_1 \ = \text{tensile strength};$$

$$R_e = P_e/A_1 = \text{rupture stress};$$

$$R_r = P_e/A_2 = \text{true rupture stress}.$$

In the table we given the results of our tests in so far as they are of interest for this investigation.

Diameter d in mm.	Contraction per cent	Tensile strength R in kg./mm.²	True rupture stress R_r in kg./mm.²	Rupture stress R_e in kg./mm.²
20	59·5	43·5	77·5	$0\cdot405 \times 77\cdot5 = 31\cdot4$
15	60	42·8	75·0	$0\cdot4 \times 75\cdot0 \ \ = 30$
10	64·3	43·5	85·5	$0\cdot357 \times 85\cdot5 = 30\cdot5$
7	68	44·0	97·5	$0\cdot32 \times 97\cdot5 \ \ = 31\cdot2$
	Average	43·3		Average 30·8

The rupture stress R_e was 70·5 per cent of the tensile strength R, which is noteworthy. From the last column it follows that between the limits of these tests the reinforcement by cold-working is proportional to the contraction and local elongation, i.e. to the specific deformation.

The skin effect on contraction was a remarkable discovery. But years ago another series of tests showed that even with a wider range the true rupture stress was raised in exact proportion to the specific deformation. These tests were repeated with great care, in 1935, by W. G. E. Tummers, a physical engineer of the State Mines.

Differences in contraction were obtained by varying the ratio of breadth to width of tensile bars with rectangular cross-section. The contraction decreased from 71·8 per cent for square bars to only 38·7 per cent for flat strips with a breadth to width ratio of 40/1. The tensile strength was always the same, but the true rupture stress increased in proportion to the contraction.

But we see the most striking confirmation of our hypothesis that reinforcement by cold-working is proportional to deformation at rupture, in the control of brittle rupture under three-dimensional stress as will be given in the next chapter, § 2. And with this increase of the true stress of rupture of the steel to more than double we are not even at the limit of possible reinforcement. If annealed soft iron is drawn to wire through a well-lubricated die in small steps so that the diameter is reduced in the proportion 3 to 1, the tensile strength is raised from 40 kg./mm.^{2} to 120 kg./mm^2, and the true stress of rupture in the same proportion. It is well known that the tensile strength of metals may be much raised by cold-working.*

Excessive deformation can only be obtained by pressure. The thin sheets of cold-rolled Siemens-Martin steel used for the manufacture of tin-plate in the United States are as hard as spring steel. Normalized at 900° C. they are almost as supple as paper and must be lightly cold-rolled again to be serviceable. It is useful for the engineer to know that under excessive pressure, plastic metals may be deep-drawn or moulded to a large extent.

2. The moulds for the manufacture of objects of Bakelite or other plastics are mostly made by the following procedure:

First a model of the object is made from the best obtainable tool steel and hardened. Thereupon this model is pressed into the block of steel which may be cold or red-hot. If it be cold-pressed, then a tough quality of tool steel is used with a tensile strength of 80 to 90

* P. Ludwik: "Festigkeit und Materialprüfung", Zeitschr. der Ver. deutscher Ing. 1924, p. 212.

kg./mm.^{2} when annealed and about 140 kg./mm.^{2} when hardened.

In Chap. XV, § 1, we calculated for fig. 87 that at an average pressure $p = 2.57s_0$ the punch enters the steel, and we showed that the shape of the underside was unimportant.

Practice has shown that a good impression is obtained at about 15,000 kg./cm.^{2} * If we calculate the yield stress from this figure we find $15,000/2.57 = 5850$ kg./cm.^{2}, which is very good for this kind of steel when annealed. It must be kept in mind that in pressing the model into the block, its dimensions are somewhat altered.

The cold-pressing or drawing of metals is a question of limiting tensile stresses and raising compressive stresses. If this is realized almost every deformation may be obtained.

Under tension alone rupture occurs at relatively small deformation. In a tensile test on strip iron, rupture (at angles of 35°, not 45° to the cross-section) occurs first in the central portion because the matter can only flow to that part of the cross-section from both sides, while at the edges it flows from three sides, which permits a greater elongation.

When we have to deal with grooved bars for which the contraction is much impeded, the steel is little reinforced, and the true stress of rupture falls to a value near the tensile strength.

3. This is the place to mention that for materials which harden considerably on cold-working, our law of plastic flow, stating that two principal stresses are equal, fails.

The theory evolved in Chap. XIII only holds true when by the deformation which accompanies the equalization of two stresses $s_1 - s_3$ or the maximum shearing stress drops. This drop is at most in the ratio $1/\sqrt{3}$ to $\frac{1}{2}$ or from 1.157 to 1 when we keep to fig. 6, and more if the difference between upper and lower yield point is taken into account.

If the strain-hardening exceeds 15.7 per cent, the law of flow is different from that on which this treatise is based. For that law we refer to the work of Hilda Geiringer and Willy Prager,† that of W. Prager,‡ of M. A. Sadowski § and H. W. Swift.‖ But for most materials, pottery-clay, ductile metals, &c., our law holds true.

* 500-ton Mould-Hobbing Press, *Engineering*, 20th Oct., 1939, p. 453.

† *Ergebnisse der exakten Naturwissenschaften*, 13, pp. 310–63, 1934.

‡ "Strain Hardening under Combined Stresses", *Journal of Applied Physics*, Vol. 16, Dec. 1935, pp. 837–40.

§ "A Principle of Maximum Plastic Resistance", *Journal of Applied Mechanics*, presented at the Annual Meeting of the American Society of Mechanical Engineers, Nov. 30–Dec. 4, 1945.

‖ "Plastic Strain in Isotropic Strain-hardening Material", *Engineering*, 18th Oct., 1946, pp. 381–4.

CHAPTER XX

The Occurrence of so-called Brittle Rupture in Plastic Material

1. In the area of rupture of mild-steel structural parts two different regions may be discerned, one of fibrous appearance which looks as if it is torn and deformed, and the other rather granulated with glittering facets, suggesting that separation takes place along the boundaries of the crystallites.

An examination was made of broken tensile bars, previously grooved in a similar manner to the compression pieces shown in figs. 91 and 92, Chap. XVI. (Diameter of cylindrical bar 20 mm., diameter at groove bottom 10 mm.) Six bars were sawn from the length after different degrees of elongation (the sixth after rupture) and etched. Here are some of the experimental results.*

1. The test bars underwent considerable deformation at the groove. As shown in fig. 105, which was taken just before rupture, the sharp-bottomed groove became cylindrical.

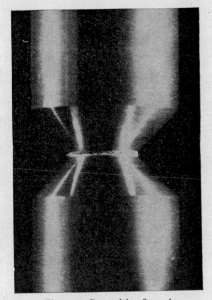

Fig. 105.—Grooved bar fissured at the bottom of the groove as a result of tension

2. Near the rupturing load, cracks became visible in the groove bottom. Perhaps the quasi-cylindrical appearance must be explained by excessive elongation causing laceration of the steel.

---

* W. Kuntze: " Kohesionsfestigkeit ", *Sonderheft XX Staatl. Materialprüfungsamt,* Berlin, 1932; A. Thum und F. Wunderlich: " Fliessgrenze bei behinderter Formänderung ", *Forschung auf dem Gebiete des Ingenieurswesens,* Band 3, 1932, Heft 6. The best and most convincing experiments have been made by Dr. P. Schoenmaker in the laboratories of Transformatorenfabriek Smit, Nijmegen.

3. After the bottom of the groove begins to tear the load may still be increased, and then the bar suddenly breaks with a loud report.

4. The granular central region of the area of rupture (fig. 106) had an average radius $r_n = 3\cdot68$ mm., and was surrounded by a greyish annular zone with an outer radius $r_0 = 4\cdot47$ mm. By contraction, the outer radius in the bottom of the groove, which was $r_i = 4\cdot85$ mm. before the test was reduced to $r_0 = 4\cdot47$ mm., measured on the broken parts of the test piece.

5. In the above-cited publication of Thum and Wunderlich, which contains illustrations bearing out the results of our investigation, we read about the etchings:

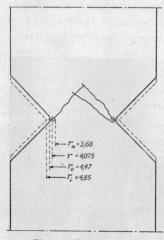

Fig. 106.—Deformation and etching lines for a tensile test on a grooved bar.

"First, two small, dark, lance-shaped marks appear near the bottom of the groove. At the last moment before the weakened section breaks down, two lines jump up from these spots at an inclination of 45°." In fig. 106 we have drawn these lines according to the photograph of Thum and Wunderlich, although our own lines were more regular and straight These lines are neither lines of rupture nor slip lines. They are only black streaks showing thin layers of plastification in the sound steel before rupture.

6. All the grooved test pieces and also several cylindrical ones were turned from the same bar and heated for 15 minutes at 900° C. The steel was uniform in quality.

Tensile strength (highest point in fig. 4) calculated from the original cross-section, $R = 44\cdot55$ kg./mm.²

Rupture stress calculated from the original cross-section (end-point in fig. 4), $R_e = 33\cdot6$ kg./mm.²

Limit of elasticity or yield stress $s_0 = 30\cdot15$ kg./mm.²

Contraction 66 per cent.

Load for rupture of grooved bar $P = 4775$ kg.

Area of grooved cross-section before test $= 73\cdot8$ mm.²

Area of grooved cross-section after test $F_0 = 62\cdot8$ mm.²

Area of coarse-grained part of section of rupture $= 42\cdot5$ kg./mm.²

Average tensile strength $P/F_0 = R_a = 76\cdot1$ kg./mm.²

2. With the knowledge of the theory of plasticity we have acquired, we ought to try to calculate the ratio of the area of granular appearance to the total area of rupture, and the breaking strength.

This might be done in the following way:

When the cracks in the bottom of the groove grow deeper, the arrow-like marks enlarge, the material is reinforced by work-hardening, and at the same time, as we shall see, the axial tension in the central portion of the section increases. But as the crack becomes deeper, the resisting area decreases. Rupture occurs with almost explosion-like violence when the maximum load is attained. The explanation of the phenomenon of rupture is mainly to be sought in the considerable increase in axial tension in the central part during the development of the arrow-like flow regions. As we are unable to establish the increase of axial tension with the deepening of the cracks, we cannot fix this maximum, but must confine ourselves to the calculation of the stresses at the moment of rupture.

The mean radius between r_0 and r_n (see fig. 106 and § **1**, section 4) is $r = 4\cdot075$ mm. Hence the area of the resisting part of the annular section is $\pi(4\cdot075^2 - 3\cdot68^2) = 9\cdot65$ mm.^{2}

The increase in strength by work-hardening is considerable. The section shrunk by about one-third, and as, according to the preceding chapter, the increase in strength is proportional to the deformation, the average stress of rupture was $1\cdot5 \times 33\cdot6 = 50\cdot5$ kg./mm.^{2} We have shown in Chap. XVI that the principal stress in the resisting part of the annular area beside the crack is obtained by multiplying by $(1 + \pi/2)$. Thus the principal stress is $2\cdot57 \times 50\cdot5 = 130$ kg./mm.^{2}

What might be the axial principal stress s_1 in the granular central part of the reduced section at the moment of rupture? The author has made many experiments to test the theories of rupture and also tried out the experiments described in literature. This subject will be dealt with in Chap. XXI. At first we infer that brittle rupture occurs according to the hypothesis of Mariotte, better known as that of Poncelet, namely, that the greatest specific elongation is the criterion of rupture.

In the biconical central part we have to deal with three-dimensional stress. We know the radial stress at the periphery. This is exerted by the tension $s_2 = 1\cdot57R_r$ in the arrow-like part of the longitudinal section (R_r denoting the stress in the steel due to work-hardening). Now this work-hardening is not equally distributed. The specific deformation on which it depends is a maximum at the bottom of the groove and at the region of the arrow-like marks it is least. For determining the tensions in the double central cone, the value of R_r in the annular space near the points of the arrow-like marks is decisive. Instead of taking $R_r = 1.5R_e$ as was done for the average tension in the annular ring, we now take $R_r = 1.2R_e$, whence $R_r = 1.2 \times 33.6 = 40.3$ kg./mm.^{2}

For a radially-stressed body, the radial and tangential stresses are the same. Therefore we know in the double cone that

$$s_2 = s_3 = 1.57 \times 40.3 = 63.3 \text{ kg./mm.}^2$$

Considering the stresses originating in the biconical core from the radial pull of the annular plastified region, it seems that these stresses are only of great magnitude when the plastic ring is well developed. This explains the occurrence of a maximum.

According to Poncelet's hypothesis of rupture with $1/m = 0.3$, steel of a tensile strength of 44.55 kg./mm.^{2} only breaks in this case of three-dimensional stress when s_1 reaches the value

$$44.55 + 0.3 \times 2 \times 63.5 = 82.65 \text{ kg./mm.}^2$$

It is noteworthy that the stress of rupture in the core is almost doubled when radial and tangential stress are fully developed.

The aggregate axial load on the grooved bar which leads to rupture for the outer plastified annular region and the brittle central core amounts to

$$P = 9.65 \times 130 + 42.5 \times 82.65 = 4760 \text{ kg.,}$$

which agrees closely with the test result.

At a later date our own tests were fully confirmed by a series of carefully made tests by Dr. P. Schoenmaker and his collaborators at N. V. Willem Smit's Transformatorenfabriek at Nijmegen and by some fine tests of Dr. v. d. Willigen of Philips at Eindhoven.

For sufficiently deep round grooves of 60° vertical angle the values of R_a were always between 1.6 and $1.65R$ (notation given at the end of § 1).

For the central core which broke like a brittle material under three-dimensional stress, Mariotte-Poncelet's criterion of rupture was confirmed in all these experiments. We recall this statement in Chap. XXI, §§ 4 and 5.

3. The fibrous torn conical outer region and the granular brittle flat inner region may be seen more clearly in the cone-and-cup rupture of cylindrical test bars of mild steel than for the grooved bar. For this

typical appearance of rupture the theory of plasticity must also provide the explanation. In the tensile test the steel flows at least at the
periphery until rupture occurs. In this case we may apply the theory
of plastic flow provided we introduce the tensile strength R instead
of the yield stress s_0. In order to keep the problem simple, we neglect
the difference between R and R_e (fig. 4). When the
load is increased necking proceeds until rupture
occurs with a loud report.

What happens at that moment?

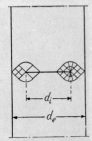

Later we shall introduce necking and work-
hardening, but first we refer to fig. 107, and calculate
the distribution of stresses assuming that the section
of rupture is not reduced. At the sides of failures in
steel, pores, slag-inclusions and stress concentrations
are met. In the interior, under three-dimensional
stress conditions, in consequence of these stress concentrations brittle rupture occurs along the boundaries of the crystallites according to the hypothesis

Fig. 107.—The
rupture of a test
bar starts inside
the material.

of Poncelet. Local fissures unite in a central rent. But around this
transverse crack we still must apply Poncelet's formula. At the edge
the ideal principal stress therefore is (Chap. V, fig. 31)

$$s_i = s_1 - \frac{s_2 + s_3}{m}; \quad s_1 = 2 \cdot 57R, \quad s_2 = s_3 = 1 \cdot 57R.$$

$$\frac{1}{m} = 0 \cdot 3, \quad s_i = s_1 \left(1 - 2 \times 0 \cdot 3 \times \frac{1 \cdot 57}{2 \cdot 57}\right) = 0 \cdot 633 s_1, \quad s_i = R,$$

hence
$$s_1 = 1 \cdot 58R.$$

Beside the central crack the steel shows an apparent tensile stress
of $1 \cdot 58R$.

In the layers at some distance below and above the cross-section of
future rupture, the steel still flows under the tension R. We therefore
have the equality

$$\left(\frac{\pi d_e^2}{4} - \frac{\pi d_i^2}{4}\right) 1 \cdot 58R = \frac{\pi d_e^2}{4} R.$$

From this we obtain $d_i = 0 \cdot 6 d_e$, which agrees fairly well with the
ratio found for the cup-and-cone rupture shown in fig. 108 for a bar of
40 mm. diameter where $d_i = 0 \cdot 56 d_e$. The photograph and the dimensions were taken at the Institut du Génie Civil of the University of

Liége. But we have many other records which bear out that the ratio
is 0·6.

If the contraction had been taken into account the result would
be the same, because work-hardening is the same at the section of
rupture and also at nearby sections.

Fig. 108.—Cup-and-cone rupture as a result of a tensile test on mild steel

But why must the iron be torn like a truncated cone at an angle of
55° with the wall?

At the end of § 4, Chap. XVIII, we have shown that this is the
inclination for which the planes of rupture show a preference under
plastic conditions.

It is essential for the explanation of the cup-and-cone rupture that,
till the last moment, the material shows little preference for plastic
flow or brittle rupture both calculated by the same tensile strength
R or R_e.

CHAPTER XXI

The Theory of Rupture

1. In this treatise no more will be said about rupture than is dictated by the principles of plasticity. We shall omit the theory of the rupture of brittle materials, which break under compression by tensile stresses at flaws in the structure, and shall deal only with the rupture of ductile matter which occurs when plastic flow ceases. This kind of fracture, which may also occur in so-called brittle material under unequal pressure, can be explained by a hypothesis of rupture which is confirmed by experiment. The formulation is due to the seventeenth-century French physicist Mariotte. In the beginning of last century attention was drawn to it by the French mathematician and engineer Poncelet, and it was generally adopted on the Continent.

We express this law of rupture as follows:

At a given temperature, the greatest elongation in the material in consequence of three-dimensional stress is the criterion for brittle rupture.

It is impossible to verify this law by tests on brittle materials, at any rate in the customary manner. Many experimenters have measured the stresses at the surface of bars under tension by means of X-rays * but the results were mostly confused. Although these experiments were made with ductile metals it is known that the stress conditions at the surface of the material are quite different from those at a small depth. We have already mentioned surface tension, but a slight polish may give rise to compression. Moreover, the surface shows numerous faults in structure as is revealed by examination with the electron microscope. The stress concentrations resulting from these flaws or faults may be estimated to amount to two or three times the calculated stresses. Not only the inter- and intra-crystalline surface failures but also many defects and irregularities within the material, make it impossible to test the law of Mariotte-Poncelet-De St. Venan by tensile or bending tests on brittle material.

---

* Bollenrath and collaborators: *Zeitschr. der Ver. deutscher Ingenieure*, 1939, p. 129, and 1940, p. 539. Much better results have been obtained by A. Schaar, " Kristallitverformung an der Oberfläche bei statischer Zug und Druckbeanspruchung ", *Zeitschr. für Metallkunde*, 1944, p. 70.

The reader ought to make some simple tests on glass bars or to read the famous communications of Griffith * on this subject to be convinced that this law does not apply to the rupture of brittle matter. It is also very instructive to investigate experimentally the existence of stresses of a different nature at the surface of bars of annealed mild steel. We mention some curious facts.

(a) In a compression test on polished cylinders, the Hartmann lines appear long before the yield stress is reached and form screw-lines on the surface sloping at 35°. The interior is not affected.

(b) In a tension test on similar bars plastic layers occur throughout, marked as ellipses on the surface of the cylinders. Their inclination to the normal cross-section is 35°.

(c) When an annealed tensile bar, which ought not to be polished, is loaded to about three-quarters of the yield stress, then sawn longitudinally and etched, short small black streaks, originating at the wall, become visible at regular intervals, showing that the yield limit in the wall is attained at an early stage.

(d) As already stated in Chap. XVI, § 3, the superficial tension at rupture must be taken into account. This tension can be calculated when two or more tensile tests on wires of different diameter are made. Textbooks, for instance Hütte I, 1936, pp. 700–1, mention that the tensile strength of wires is represented by the formula

$$R = R_0 + \frac{c}{d},$$

d being the diameter of the wire.

When we express the values in kg. and cm. we find for annealed steel wire

$$R = 5730 + \frac{38}{d} \text{ kg./cm.}^2;$$

for tungsten wire $R = 19{,}000 + \frac{69}{d} \text{ kg./cm.}^2$

For the latter metal this gives a tensile strength of 65,000 kg./cm.² for a diameter of 0·015 mm.

For wires of quartz and glass this phenomenon has been especially well studied.† The special conditions prevailing at the surface of rock

* A. A. Griffith: " The theory of rupture ", *Proc. of the 1st International Congress for Applied Mechanics*, p. 55, Delft, 1925; *Handbuch der Phyik*, Vol. VI, p. 455.

† S. Shurkow: *Physikalische Zeitschr. der Sowjetunion*, Vol. 1, p. 123, Charkow, 1932; Griffith: *Phil. Trans. Roy. Soc.*, 221, III, p. 164 (1923).

salt lead to rupture in a tensile test, long before the breaking strength within is reached. This has been proved by Joffé,* and explains why tensile tests without a high surrounding pressure are unsuitable for investigations on the laws of rupture. But it will be shown that Poncelet's law of rupture (the maximum strain theory) may be tested by eliminating the influence of surface tension, and of external and internal faults, and making the experiments under a surrounding pressure of sufficient magnitude. The details of many experiments of this kind have been published.

2. We avail ourselves of some famous and reliable tests †; in the first place the classical experiments made by von Kármán, with marble, for which material m was found to be 3·7. We express the stresses in kg./cm.² and calculate the ideal stress

$$s_i = s_1 - \frac{s_2 + s_3}{m}.$$

No.	s_1	s_2	s_3	s_i
1	− 235	− 235	−2300	+450
2	− 500	− 500	−3150	+485
3	− 685	− 685	−3485	+440
4	− 845	− 845	−3910	+440
5	−1650	−1650	−6090	+440

All in kg./cm.²

Further, we use the results of experiments on cement mortar made in the laboratory for testing materials at Zürich for which $m = 4\cdot2$. This high value of m is due to 11 per cent porosity.

No.	s_1	s_2	s_3	s_i
1	−100	−100	− 935	147
2	−350	−350	−1700	140
3	−510	−510	−2240	145

All in kg./cm.²

* A. Joffé: *The Physics of Crystals*, New York, 1928.

† *Versuche dur Klärung der Frage der Bruchgefahr*, von Ros und Eichinger, II, " Nichtmetallische Stoffe. Eidgenössische Materialprüfungsanstalt zu der E. T. H. Zürich ", 1928, p. 10 and fig. 32, then p. 20 and fig. 47, and p. 18 and fig. 43.

And lastly, we have experiments with pure cement for which $m = 4.4$, caused by 28 per cent porosity.

No.	s_1	s_2	s_3	s_i
1	-45	-45	-555	91
2	-355	-355	-1525	73
3	-635	-635	-2485	75

All in kg./cm.^{2}

The first of each series of tests was generally made with insufficient surrounding pressure. If this is omitted Poncelet's law is fully confirmed. But this law may also be tested for brittle materials which are somewhat plastic, so that small faults at the surface or within are eliminated. Perfect agreement must not be expected in this case. Take, for instance, cast iron, for which Bach * found that the rupture stress at compression, tension and torsion are in proportion:

$$R_2 : R_1 : R_3 = 4 : 1 : 0.8 \quad \text{with} \quad m = 4.$$

He pointed out that the formula

$$s_i = s_1 - \frac{s_2 + s_3}{m}$$

gives for compression

$$s_1 = 0, \quad s_2 = 0, \quad s_3 = -R_3 \quad s_i = \frac{R_2}{4} = R:$$

for tension $\quad s_1 = R_1, \quad s_2 = 0, \quad s_3 = 0, \quad s_i = R_1 = R;$

for torsion

$$s_1 = R_3, \quad s_2 = 0, \quad s_3 = -R_3, \quad s_i = 1.25R_3 = R.$$

More evidence is provided by later investigations.† Ros and Eichinger mention at the beginning of p. 14 that m increased from 3.7 to 7.4 and from 3.3 to 6.5. We take $m = 6$ and calculate s_i according to a series of tests given in Table IV.

Tests 3, 4 and 5 were made on hollow tubes, 6, 7 and 8 are torsion tests.

---

* Bach: *Elastizität und Festigkeit*, 1911, p. 166 and p. 324.

† Ros und Eichinger: *Versuche zur Klärung der Bruchgefahr*, III, " Metalle ", 1929.

No.	s_1	s_2	s_3	s_i
1	1740	−175	−3890	$1740 + \dfrac{4065}{6} = 2420$
2	1700	−170	−3900	$1700 + \dfrac{4070}{6} = 2380$
3	1700	−170	−3770	$1700 + \dfrac{3940}{6} = 2360$
4	2025	−205	−2360	$2025 + \dfrac{2565}{6} = 2465$
5	2025	−205	−2240	$2025 + \dfrac{2445}{6} = 2430$
6	2140	0	−2140	$(1 + \tfrac{1}{6})\, 2140 = 2500$
7	2120	0	−2120	$1 \cdot 167 \times 2120 = 2470$
8	2110	0	−2120	$1 \cdot 167 \times 2110 = 2460$

All in kg./cm.^{2}

If all the 20 tests are checked with the law of Mariotte-Poncelet the agreement is at least as good. That the average tensile strength 2215 kg./cm.^{2} and the average compressive strength 8495 kg./cm.^{2} are somewhat less in accordance to this law may be explained by the facts:

1°. The porosity has a greater influence on strength in a tensile test than in a test with compound stresses.

2°. The bulging in the compressive test causes extra stresses which are not taken into account. Cast iron in tension always breaks at pores, slag inclusions or flaws.

The author has carried out many experiments on bars of the shape shown in fig. 75 and other shapes, made from an alloy consisting of 75 per cent Pb, 23 per cent Sb and 2 per cent Sn (elongation 0 per cent) and obtained $m = 4$, a good confirmation of Poncelet's law. We attach much importance to the statement at the end of § 2 of the previous chapter, that ductile materials breaking with a brittle rupture under three-dimensional stress also confirm Poncelet's law.

3. Some confusion exists on the condition of plastic flow and the condition of rupture. We therefore repeat that **for all materials, brittle as well as ductile, plastic flow sets in when the criterion of Maxwell is fulfilled, i.e.**

$$s_1{}^2 + s_2{}^2 + s_3{}^2 - s_2 s_3 - s_3 s_1 - s_1 s_2 = s_0{}^2;$$

and that in brittle and ductile material, rupture always occurs according to the criterion of Poncelet, i.e. when

$$s_1 - \frac{s_2 + s_3}{m} = R.$$

This applies to static tests.

It may be asked whether a constant relation exists between the rupture stress for tension or bending and for torsion in fatigue tests. The investigation of this subject by the National Physical Laboratory * gave a perfect confirmation of Maxwell's formula for mild steel with 0·1 per cent of carbon.

The repeated stress tests gave $R_3 = 0.58R_1$.

The same result has been obtained by many experimenters in different countries † for several ductile metals. *It is now a well-established fact that the criterion of Maxwell for the beginning of plastic yield also holds true for the breakdown under fatigue of ductile metals.* Repeated plastic yield destroys the material.

For brittle materials undergoing fatigue tests it seems that the criterion of Mariotte-Poncelet must be applied. On the Continent as well as in England and America $R_3 = 0.93R$ has been found for cast iron. For $m = 4$ this relation ought to have been $R_3 = 0.8R$, but m generally is greater than 4 due to the porosity of cast iron and also because irregularities in the structure seem to have more influence in repeated bending than in repeated twisting.

4. We have now to deduce the law according to which materials, considered as brittle, become plastic at normal temperature. But first we calculate when annealed mild steel breaks like a brittle material.

In order to simplify the calculation we assume (fig. 4) that the yield stress is half the tensile strength, i.e. $s_0 = 0.5R$. And dealing only with common applications we take two principal stresses equal, here $s_2 = s_3$. For steel, $m = 10/3$.

According to Poncelet, rupture occurs when

$$s_1 - \frac{s_2 + s_3}{m} = R.$$

According to Maxwell plastic yield occurs when

$$s_1 - s_3 = s_0 = 0.5R.$$

---

* *Engineering*, 12th July, 1935, p. 44.

† *La fatigue des Métaux par Cazaux et Persoz* (Paris, 1943), pp. 88–9. A long list of literature on this subject is published in Metallwirtschaft, XX, No. 38 (1941), pp. 931–7.

The material hesitates and rupture and yield limit coincide when both equations are fulfilled at the same time, i.e. when

$$s_1 - 0 \cdot 6 s_3 = R, \quad s_1 - s_3 = 0 \cdot 5R \quad \text{or} \quad s_1 = 1 \cdot 75R, \quad s_2 = s_3 = 1 \cdot 25R.$$

Mild steel with a tensile strength of $R = 40$ kg./mm.^{2} breaks under three-dimensional tension when

$$s_1 = 70 \text{ kg./mm.}^2, \quad s_2 = s_3 = 50 \text{ kg./mm.}^2$$

or expressed more exactly, it is then at the margin of plastic deformation and elastic rupture. It certainly behaves like a brittle material when

$$s_2 = s_3 > 50 \text{ kg./mm.}^2$$

5. By work-hardening the yield limit may be raised. When a bar is cold-strained above the yield point and the load removed, the yield limit becomes $s_0 = \sigma R$. For work-hardened mild steel σ may be situated between 0·5 and 1(0·5 $< \sigma <$ 1).

Now we repeat the calculation of the former paragraph for $s_0 = \sigma R$ and find

$$s_1 - \frac{2}{m} s_3 = R; \quad s_1 - s_3 = \sigma R;$$

$$s_1 = \frac{m - 2\sigma}{m - 2} R; \quad s_2 = s_3 = \frac{m - m\sigma}{m - 2} R.$$

If $\sigma = 1$, when by work-hardening the ductility has been exhausted, these relations become

$$s_1 = R, \quad s_2 = s_3 = 0.$$

To obtain a brittle rupture in a tensile test on mild steel the specimen should be first drawn and hammered to maximum elongation.

6. The so-called brittle materials differ from the ductile in the property of breaking without preliminary plastic deformation in a tensile, bending or twisting test under atmospheric pressure. But this is only an apparent difference. Tested under sufficient surrounding pressure all materials become plastic. Mathematically expressed, a material is brittle when

$$s_0 > R \quad \text{or} \quad s_0 = \sigma R \text{ for } \sigma > 1.$$

The author made some interesting tests demonstrating that concrete and hardened cement mortar may be plastically deformed. When do these materials become ductile?

Let us call the lateral pressure s_1, which is equal to s_2. This is the greatest principal stress, and the axial pressure on the test piece (of greater magnitude s_3) is, in an absolute sense, the smallest pressure, as all tensions are negative. Rupture occurs according to Poncelet when

$$s_i = s_1 - \frac{s_2 + s_3}{m} = R.$$

Plastic deformation occurs when $s_1 - s_3 = s_0 = \sigma R$.

We are at the limit of brittle rupture and plastic deformation when both equations are fulfilled at the same moment, that is, when

$$s_1 = s_2 = \frac{m - \sigma}{m - 2} R, \quad s_3 = \frac{\sigma - (\sigma - 1)m}{m - 2} R.$$

For cement mortar (see § 2), $m = 4 \cdot 2$, $R = 145$ kg./cm.², and we can add $\sigma = 8$. So we find that the cement mortar becomes plastic when the lateral pressure exceeds

$$s_1 = s_2 = -250 \text{ kg/cm.}^2$$

A pressure on the end of the test block of less than

$$s_3 = -1160 \text{ kg./cm.}^2$$

will then start plastic flow.

Rock salt and slate become plastic at about the same pressure. For other materials like marble with $m = 3 \cdot 7$, $R = 440$ kg./cm.², $\sigma = 7$, we need higher pressures, but it is certain that in the earth's crust at relatively small depths every kind of rock is perfectly plastic.

The theories of elasticity and plasticity belong to the basis of scientific mining,* but are unable to explain the current effects of earth pressure. The theory of stress distribution in incoherent masses is much more in accordance with reality. However, the first-named theories must be mastered before this more intricate subdivision of applied mechanics can be studied.

---

* " Les tensions autour de cavités d'après la théorie de l'élasticité. La pression du toit sur le charbon ", *Revue Universelle des Mines*, 1941; *Proceedings Royal Netherlands Academy of Sciences*, 1939 and 1940.

CHAPTER XXII

Rupture at Sharp Incisions

All material can rupture in two ways:

1. Through plastic flow, according to the law of Maxwell amended by the author, i.e. with perfect plasticity, flowing and contracting like heated glass while the difference between two principal stresses remains equal to the yield stress.

2. With a sudden rupture, according to the law of Mariotte-Poncelet, when the greatest strain (extension) reaches the breaking strain. What happens when the load on our structural part is gradually increased depends on which of the criteria is first fulfilled.

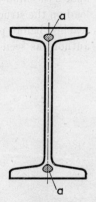

Fig. 109.—Beam with cores under high tension.

At the free surface of a mild-steel beam one of the principal stresses, called s_3, is zero.

When s_2, another principal stress, is also zero, the material flows when the only principal stress s is equal to the yield stress. If another principal stress exists, the greatest strain is even less and the danger of sudden rupture is still smaller. Hence we come to the peculiar conclusion that a breakdown in plastic material, for instance in mild steel, will never start at the surface. But a brittle rupture—a sudden laceration—may occur in the interior of such material at a spot where three-dimensional tension prevails.

Imagine a hot-rolled steel beam rapidly cooled (fig. 109). It may be that the thin rib first solidifies and then the tips of the flanges. These parts cool down further while cores at a of the section are still red-hot. When these cores also become solid they fit in under a negligible tension. Let us suppose that the cores are only 100° C. hotter than the material farther off which is already blue-warm; and then the temperature equalizes. The core tends to shrink and with the modulus of elasticity $E = 2,000,000$ kg./cm.^{2}, Poissons modulus $m = \dfrac{10}{3}$, and the coefficient of expansion $\alpha = 0.00001$, the tension in all directions would be 5000 kg./cm.^{2} This is not so harmful as it looks because the ideal tension according to Mariotte-Poncelet would only be $5000\left(1 - \dfrac{2}{m}\right) = 2000$ kg./cm.² But this high tension in all directions

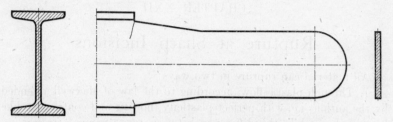

Fig. 110.—Rents which occurred when a beam was cut by an oxy-acetylene torch

makes the mild-steel beam liable to brittle fracture. By superposing a load on the structure there is a chance that the breaking strain may be reached before plastic flow sets in, and in fact this often happens. The author has seen sixteen ruptures when the flanges of four beams were

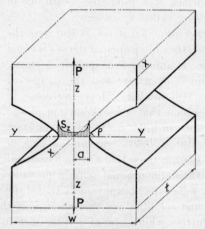

Fig. 111.—Bar under tension with grooves of hyperbolic shape

cut at both ends by the oxy-acetylene torch (represented in fig. 110). The rents in the rib starting from the danger spot were due to the expansion of the flanges when they were heated.

But why does a brittle rupture often spread in a plastic material? The question is so important in engineering that it must be amply discussed.

Brittle fracture in mild steel indicates tension stress in every direction. We therefore have to infer the occurrence of three-dimensional stress near the ends of cracks. In order to prove the existence of such stresses we start from the stress distribution according to the laws of elastic deformation and tensions near the bottom of incisions. Since Inglis solved the problem by means of elliptic co-ordinates we may refer to the literature.*

Let fig. 111 represent a stretched bar of great length in the direction of the X-axis. The grooves at both sides are hyperbolic, according to the formula

$$\frac{y^2}{a^2} - \frac{z^2}{b^2} = 1.$$

If we consider a section of this bar of length t and suppose the pull to be P, then the average tension in the weakened section is $p = \dfrac{P}{2at}$.

The radius of curvature in the bottom of the groove is $\rho = \dfrac{b^2}{a}$.

Transformed from elliptic co-ordinates to orthogonal co-ordinates, the principal tensions in the danger section are

$$s_z = \frac{(a^2 + 2a\rho - y^2)\,(a^2 + a\rho)}{(a^2 + a\rho - y^2)^{\frac{3}{2}} \left\{ (a + p \text{ arc tan} \sqrt{\dfrac{a}{\rho}} + \sqrt{a\rho} \right\}}\, p,$$

$$s_y = \frac{(a^2 - y^2)\,(a^2 + a\rho)}{(a^2 + a\rho - y^2)^{\frac{3}{2}} \left\{ (a + \rho) \text{ arc tan} \sqrt{\dfrac{a}{\rho}} + \sqrt{a\rho} \right\}}\, p,$$

$$s_x = 0{\cdot}6\, \frac{a^2 + a\rho}{(a^2 + a\rho - y^2)^{\frac{1}{2}} \left\{ (a + \rho) \text{ arc tan} \sqrt{\dfrac{a}{\rho}} + \sqrt{a\rho} \right\}}\, p.$$

This last tension s_x in the direction of the X-axis is derived from s_z and s_y, assuming that the width w and the breadth t of the bar and the incision are so great that a contraction in the length w of the endangered section may be neglected. Then $s_x = \dfrac{s_z + s_y}{m}$. For steel $m = \dfrac{10}{3}$.

* H. Neuber, *Kerbspannungslehre*, Berlin, 1937, p. 33: Die beiderseitige Aussenkerbe.

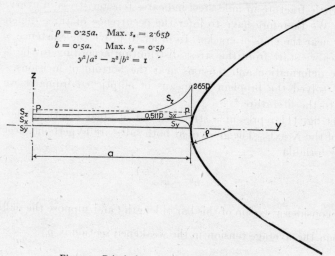

$\rho = 0.25a.$ Max. $s_z = 2.65p$
$b = 0.5a.$ Max. $s_y = 0.5p$
$y^2/a^2 - z^2/b^2 = 1$

Fig. 112.—Principal stresses in a grooved bar ($\rho = a/4$)

In figs. 112–4 the distribution of the three principal stresses is shown for half the section of the incised bar having hyperbolic grooves with curvatures at the vertex respectively

$$\rho = \frac{a}{4}, \; \rho = \frac{a}{16} \text{ and } \rho = \frac{a}{100}.$$

We see from these figures that three-dimensional tensile stress occurs in grooved bars below the bottom of the notch and that the tensions tend to infinity when ρ decreases. This was to be proved.

Now we return to the theory of plasticity.

At the bottom of the groove $s_y = 0$ and, as in plastic flow two tensions become equal, $s_x = 0$.

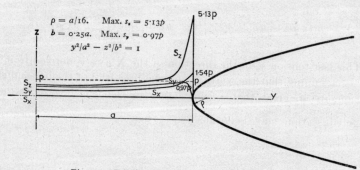

$\rho = a/16.$ Max. $s_z = 5.13p$
$b = 0.25a.$ Max. $s_y = 0.97p$
$y^2/a^2 - z^2/b^2 = 1$

Fig. 113.—Principal stresses in a grooved bar ($\rho = a/16$)

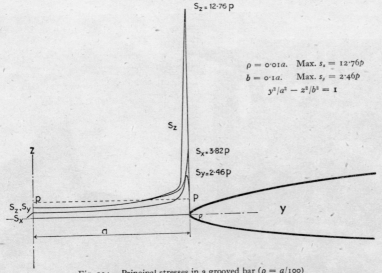

Fig. 114.—Principal stresses in a grooved bar ($\rho = a/100$)

But all three tensions rapidly increase when we enter the material. For cylindrical grooves of curvature r_0 (fig. 115) this increase of ten-

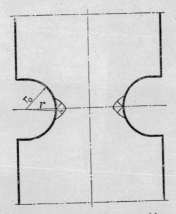

Fig. 115.—Plastic flow in a grooved bar

sions takes place according to the law $s_t = s_0\left(1 + \log_e \dfrac{r}{r_0}\right)$,

$$s_r = s_0 \log_e \frac{r}{r_0} \quad \text{and} \quad s_x = s_0 \log_e \frac{r}{r_0}.$$

Fig. 116.—This bridge girder had stood up to heavy traffic and was of excellent mild steel, yet rupture occurred without any deformation when the bridge was blown up. The fracture has a brittle appearance

s_t is double the elastic limit for $r = 2 \cdot 832 r_0$. This is very near the bottom of the groove when r_0 is small.

The differences in tension are $s_t - s_z = s_0$, and $s_t - s_x = s_0$, where s_0 represents the elastic limit or yield stress.

The steel flows at the bottom of a rounded notch, but at some distance the three-dimensional tensions become so large that the material no longer flows but breaks in a brittle manner. For sharp rents this rupture occurs very near the end of the rent. Often the rupture is explosion-like and spreads far into the material.

Fig. 116 is a photograph of a rent in a blown-up bridge girder.

The theory of brittle rupture has become of the utmost importance since it has been recognized as the basis for the study of welding. We strongly recommend the study of " Recherches, Études et Considérations sur les Constructions Soudées ",* which contains a wealth of facts on this subject and is complementary to this treatise.

* Par F. Campus, Professeur à l'Université de Liége, *Sciences et Lettres*, Liége, 1947.

CHAPTER XXIII

Applications

1. *Indentation of Curved Surfaces.*

With our acquired knowledge we have been able to solve many problems on plastic deformation and stress distribution. It may be profitable to give some more examples. We start with the analogy of the problem of fig. 16, and deal first with a cylinder of plastic material compressed on two quadrants and drawn over two others (fig. 117). As soon as the compression $-p$ and the tension p at the surface attain the value $p = k$ (in which $k = s_0/2$, half the yield stress) the cylinder becomes plastified in the regions filled with lines of maximum shearing stress. The yield shearing stress is not reached in the dotted regions except along the diagonals. Every zone is in equilibrium under the stresses along its borders. The curved shearing-stress trajectories are logarithmic spirals.

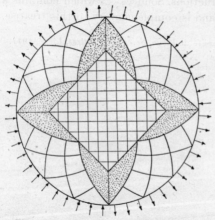

Fig. 117.—Cylinder of ductile material subjected to compression over two opposite quadrants and to tension over the other two until plastic yield occurs.

In fig. 118 we show the case where the cylinder is compressed over three sectors of 60° and drawn over three others. The reader must begin with the investigation of the hexagonal prism, for which he will find that pressures and tensions $p = \pm(1 + \pi/6)k$ on successive sides start plastification. The same stresses must be exerted on the six sectors of the cylindrical surface and lead to the trajectories shown of critical shearing stress k. When the number of sectors, alternately drawn and compressed, is increased, we at last come to the limit

$$p_e = \pm(1 + \pi/2)k.$$

If a surrounding pressure $-p_e$ is superposed, we have the case of a cylinder with sectors alternately loaded and unloaded. Omitting the load on all sectors except one, we have the analogy to fig. 16.

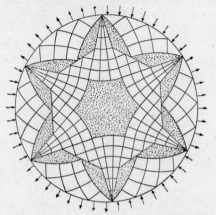

Fig. 118.—Plastic yield for a cylinder divided into six sections over three of which, symmetrically situated, compression occurs and over the other three, tension.

2. *Parallel Cylinders forced together.*

When two cylinders of equal diameter are forced together until plastic deformation occurs, planes of contact are formed.

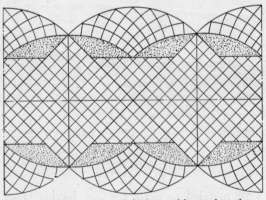

Fig. 119.—Three cylinders of plastic material pressed together until they make contact over an angle of 90°

Fig. 119 shows a number of cylinders pressed together until the plane surfaces of contact subtend a right angle at the axes of the cylinders. It can be proved that the convex parts remain cylindrical.

We suggest that the reader construct figures for the case of cylinders whose surface of contact is less developed, and that he prove that, if the diameters of the cylinders be different, the greater cylinder remains undented due to work-hardening.

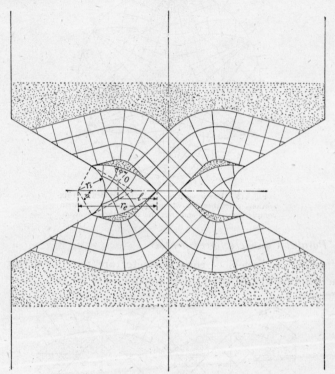

Fig. 120.—Plastic regions at the bottom of a rounded groove subjected to tension

3. *Rounding of the Bottom of the Notch.*

The calculations relative to fig. 120 are lengthy. The result obtained is that when

$$l = \frac{\phi}{1+\phi} r_e = \frac{\phi}{1+\phi} e^{\varphi} r_i,$$

test pieces with rounded or sharp notches, having O as vertex, are equivalent.

We note that the effect of rounding on the resistance of a bar of plastic material is least when the radius is not very great. It is a problem of analysis to prove that, when l has the calculated value, O is situated on the produced generating line of the notch.

4. *Square Hole in a Plastic Mass* (fig. 121).

Now we venture to give the solution for plastic flow about a hole of square section in plastic material subjected to external or internal pressure. (See Chap. V, § 2.)

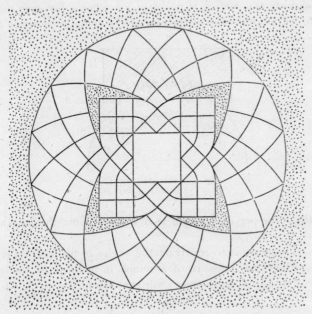

Fig. 121.—Plastification around a square hole in material subjected to external or internal pressure

We must not omit to insert non-plastified areas between plastified regions with different patterns.

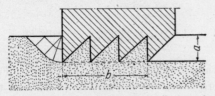

Fig. 122.—Special tool attacking tangentially the surface of plastic matter

5. *The Resistance of Plastic Material to Tangential and Oblique Forces acting on the Surface.*

The force needed to move the tool shown in fig. 122, to the left, supposing the start of the operation is in the position indicated with all the teeth biting the plastic material, is

$$K = ka\left(1 + \frac{\pi}{2}\right) + kb.$$

When only the surface is indented, i.e. when a becomes negligible, $K = kb$. Of more interest is the case of the cylinder shown in fig. 123,

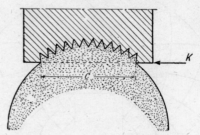

Fig. 123.—Special tool attacking a cylindrical surface

where the force per unit length is $K = kc$, c being the length of the chord.

A good exercise is to construct the angles in fig. 124, representing the case where the pressure of a punch is inclined to the vertical. Compared to fig. 16, it becomes clear that symmetry, as shown in that

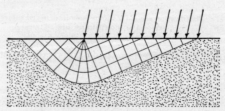

Fig. 124.—Indentation of a flat surface by inclined forces

figure, is exceptional. Fig. 16 is not really exact. For materials not subjected to work-hardening the material is inclined to be pressed up at one side only.

6. *The Thick-walled Cylinder under Internal Pressure.*

Now that we are near the end of this treatise it is worth returning to Chap. II to discuss the axial tension s_z for the thick-walled cylinder,

the data for which are indicated in fig. 125. We know from Chap. XIII
that s_z will either take the same value as s_t or s_r. The condition for
plasticity is then reduced to Coulomb's law

$$s_t - s_r = s_0,$$

and the wall is plastified throughout at the internal pressure

$$p = s_0 \log_e \frac{b}{a}.$$

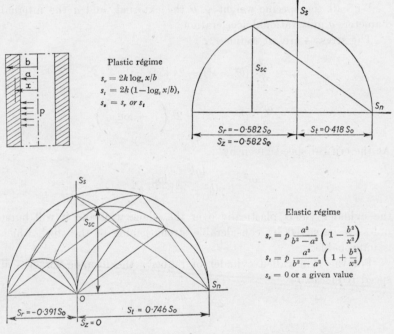

Plastic régime

$s_r = 2k \log_e x/b$
$s_t = 2k (1 - \log_e x/b),$
$s_z = s_r$ or s_t

$S_r = -0.582 S_0$
$S_z = -0.582 S_0$
$S_t = 0.418 S_0$

Elastic régime

$$s_r = p \frac{a^2}{b^2 - a^2} \left(1 - \frac{b^2}{x^2} \right)$$
$$s_t = p \frac{a^2}{b^2 - a^2} \left(1 + \frac{b^2}{x^2} \right)$$
$s_z = 0$ or a given value

$S_r = -0.391 S_0$
$S_z = 0$
$S_t = 0.746 S_0$

Fig. 125.—Thick-walled cylinder yielding to internal pressure. Below:
stress circle at the start of plastic deformation at the inside of the cylinder.
Above: stress circle for total plastification.

But at what radius does s_z jump from s_r to s_t? This depends on the
axial force in the wall.

When the pressure p is exerted by a ground plunger then the axial
force is zero, and the radius is calculated from the condition that the
region under compression is in equilibrium with the region under
tension. When the wall is axially pulled, when, for instance, the ends
of the cylinders are closed and oil is pressed in through a small hole

11

in the flanges, then the circle dividing the zones of axial tension and compression is a different one, but also easy to compute.

The agreement of theory and test results, evident from the table given in Chap. II, § 1, on experiments with axial pull confirms the statement about the mean principal stress.

7. *The Rotating Drum.*

It is a good exercise to calculate the stresses in the plastified region for a thick-walled cylinder rotating on its axis at an angular speed ω.

We call the specific weight γ, b the external, and a the internal diameter, g gravitational acceleration.

The stresses are, at radius r,

$$s_r = \frac{\omega^2 \gamma}{2g}(b^2 - r^2) - 2k \log_e \frac{b}{r},$$

$$s_t = \frac{\omega^2 \gamma}{2g}(b^2 - r^2) + 2k\left(1 - \log_e \frac{b}{r}\right).$$

At the critical speed given by

$$\omega^2 = \frac{4gk}{\gamma(b^2 - a^2)} \log_e \frac{b}{a},$$

the cylinder yields plastically over the whole wall and it will burst unless it be saved by considerable strengthening of the steel, which is improbable.

For the thin-walled cylinder of radius r the formula for critical speed reduces to

$$\omega^2 = \frac{2gk}{\gamma r^2}.$$

This is both the critical speed and the speed at which the yield limit is reached at the circumference of a rotating disc. But this does not imply that the problem of the rotating disc and of the rotating thick-walled cylinder with the same internal and external diameter are dealt with in the same way, as is done in the similar elasticity problems. According to the theory of elasticity plain stress and plain strain problems are identical. As may be understood from the preliminary remarks in Chap. V, the rotating disc is not a two-dimensional problem because dimensional change normal to its plane is not impeded.

8. *Wedge of Plastic Material loaded on One Side.*

We revert to the problem proposed in Chap. IV, § 4, and shown here in fig. 126. This is one of the exercises in the theory of plasticity. One flank of the wedge is evenly loaded by the pressure p per unit length.

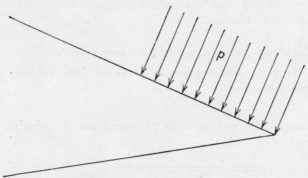

Fig 126.—Wedge loaded till plastic flow sets in

To solve the problem, it is simplified by superposing a tension $p/2$ in all directions, which makes no change in the distribution of the shearing stresses, and we have to deal with the case presented in fig. 127.

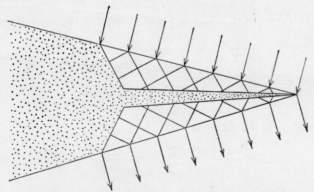

Fig. 127.—Trajectories of maximum shear stress for a wedge bent by
side-pressure evenly applied

The maximum shearing stresses always occur at angles of 45° with the principal stresses whose direction on the surfaces is known. The instantaneous picture shown in fig. 127 gives the stress distribution just before the edge succumbs.

Attention is drawn to the law of similarity holding in the plasti-fied region.

When both plastified regions touch, the trajectories meet at an angle which is contrary to the rule, and this indicates a hazardous peculiarity. This is the chief point of this paragraph.

The reader is invited to ascertain the whole stress distribution for the resistance to bending.

9. *The Plastic Mass extruded by a Contracting Cylinder.*

For the generating line of the extruded mass we find with the notation of fig. 128

$$r = r_0 e^{-\frac{x}{2l}}.$$

Plastic flow occurs with the least pressure when two principal stresses are equal, e.g. if $s_t = s_r$.

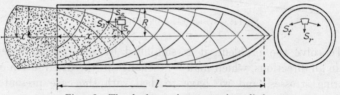

Fig. 128.—The plastic mass in a contracting cylinder

The condition of equilibrium for an element in the radial direction is

$$r \frac{\partial s_r}{\partial r} + s_r - s_t - \frac{\partial s_s}{\partial x} r = 0;$$

in the axial direction

$$r \frac{\partial s_s}{\partial r} + s_s + r \frac{\partial s_z}{\partial x} = 0.$$

The condition of plasticity is

$$\frac{(s_r - s_z)^2}{4} + s_s{}^2 = k^2,$$

and the solutions

$$s_r = s_t = -2k \frac{x}{R},$$

$$s_z = -2k \left(\frac{x}{R} + \sqrt{1 - \frac{r^2}{R^2}} \right),$$

$$s_s = k \frac{r}{R}.$$

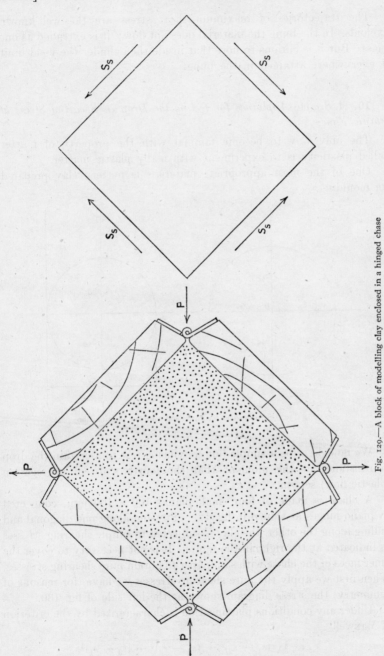

Fig. 129.—A block of modelling clay enclosed in a hinged chase

The trajectories of maximum shear stress are the well-known cycloids. In the bung the material does not flow; it is extruded as one mass. But it is curious to note that inside the cylinder the yield limit is everywhere attained in the bung.

10. *A Simple Appliance for feeling the Drop in Shearing Stress at Plastic Flow.*

The only way to become familiar with the property of matter called plasticity is to experiment with really plastic matter.

One of the most appropriate materials is pottery clay prepared for moulding.

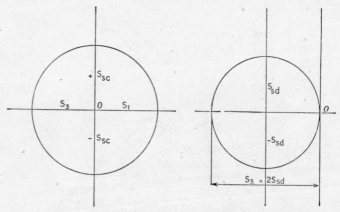

Fig. 130.—Stress circles for initial and complete plastification

We now describe a simple but convincing test to ascertain the drop in resistance at the moment that the fourth state of aggregation (plastic flow) sets in.

A chase is made of four small planks 100×100 mm. connected by piano-hinges as shown in fig. 129. Pressing along one diagonal and pulling along the other, the clay is subjected to simple shearing stresses as indicated at the right in the figure. It is not necessary to cover the inner faces of the chase with sandpaper to obtain pure shearing stresses. When first we apply the pure shearing stresses we have (for reasons of symmetry) the stress diagram shown at the left side of fig. 130.

Under any conditions plastification is characterized by the criterion of Maxwell

$$s_{sc} = \tfrac{1}{3}\sqrt{(s_1 - s_2)^2 + (s_2 - s_3)^2 + (s_3 - s_1)^2}.$$

The tension on the hands reveals when plastification starts. We call the shearing stress (fig. 129) needed for starting plastification s_{ss}, then the principal stresses (fig. 130 left) are

$$s_1 = s_{ss}, \quad s_2 = 0, \quad \text{and} \quad s_3 = -s_{ss}.$$

So the critical, characteristic shearing stress is

$$s_{sc} = \frac{\sqrt{6}}{3} s_{ss} \quad \text{or} \quad s_{ss} = \frac{3}{\sqrt{6}} s_{sc}.$$

But immediately plastic flow sets in, two principal stresses become equal and zero, and we get the stress circle represented at the right side of fig. 130.

Only one principal stress survives, and for this case we call the maximum shearing stress s_{sd}. This is the final stage, and now we have $s_1 = 0$, $s_2 = 0$, and $s_3 = 2s_{sd}$. Substituting in the criterion of Maxwell, we find

$$s_{sc} = \frac{\sqrt{8}}{3} s_{sd} \quad \text{or} \quad s_{sd} = \frac{3}{\sqrt{8}} s_{sc}.$$

The relation between s_{sd}, the maximum shearing stress at plastic flow, and s_{ss}, the maximum shearing stress at which plastification starts, is

$$s_{sd} : s_{ss} = \sqrt{8} : \sqrt{6} = 1 \cdot 157.$$

We feel the moment at which plastic flow sets in by a drop in the resistance of the clay. Therefore we call that stress the *drop shearing stress*.

This experiment is so impressive that it compels one to seek the explanation.

If we try to compress the clay further, the two free surfaces of the cube begin to bulge, the force exercised on the planks increases considerably and soon stops any movement. This phenomenon can be easily explained.

11. *The Torsion of the Solid Cylindrical Bar.*

In Chap. XVII, § 1, we accepted the usual assumption that in a solid cylindrical bar twisted until plastic yield occurs $s_1 = s$, $s_2 = 0$, and $s_3 = -s$.

This assumes that the axial tension $s_z = 0$ throughout the bar. But how can we confirm that the axial tension is zero? In plasticity it is better to distrust any analogy with elasticity and to suppose that axial stresses exist, which must be partly of tension and partly compression, making equilibrium with the axial load. In this way it becomes possible to bring the stress distribution into agreement with the condition that at plastic flow two principal stresses are equal. We want $s_1 = 2s$, $s_2 = 0$, and $s_3 = 0$.

This gives the same stress differences and the same shear stress in normal and axial section as the assumption $s_1 = s$, $s_2 = 0$, and $s_3 = -s$.

We can now calculate at what radius the axial normal stress jumps from tension to compression and find that outside

$$r = \tfrac{1}{2} r_e \sqrt{2}, \quad s_z = k,$$

and inside this radius $\qquad s_z = -k,$

where r_e is the outer radius of the bar.

We see to our astonishment that in plastic flow the shearing stress in cross-sections is accompanied at the outer fibres by a normal tension stress. This may be demonstrated by wringing a towel till it tears. It also explains a fact observed by Swift for mild steel *: " under static torsion rupture always occurs across a transverse plane and not along a longitudinal plane through the axis, although these sets of planes are subject to equal shear stress."

The case of pure torsional stress can be approximately realized by torsion of thin-walled tubes, although this kind of experiment has several inconveniences. In this way it was found that the first plastic yield occurred at $s_{sc} = 0 \cdot 578 s_0$ in agreement with the law of Maxwell-Huber-Hencky. Torsion tests on solid bars, on the other hand, give no well-determined upper yield shearing stress. But a sharp drop in load occurs at the moment of pronounced plastic flow and it is certain that yielding goes on at $s_{sp} = 0 \cdot 5 s_p$ in agreement with the law of Coulomb-Guest.

As this is the novelty of this treatise we set out the facts on which it is based without apology.

The author found the experiments described in Chap. XI, §§ 2 and 3, quite convincing, but other elaborate tests may be cited.

Smith † found tubes inappropriate for verification of the laws of yielding. His tests on solid bars under tension, compression, torsion and combinations of these types of loading provide a most striking

---

* " Tensional effects on torsional overstrain in mild steel ", *Engineering*, 20th October, 1939, p. 454, first column.

† C. A. M. Smith: " Compound Stress Experiments ", *Engineering*, 24th Dec., 1909, p. 849.

confirmation of the law of Coulomb-Guest, which is an indirect proof that at plastic flow two principal stresses become equal.

The most extended investigation on the plastic breakdown of solid cylindrical bars was made in England in 1916 by a large committee composed of the most competent specialists.* What we call the first yield, which for tubes is more or less in agreement with Maxwell's law, is called the elastic limit by this committee. They write: " The conclusion may be drawn that Guest's law does not apply to elastic limits as at present defined only to the drop stresses."

The " drop stresses " or " plastic limits " for torsion and tension, as they are termed by this committee, we call s_{sp} and s_p. They came to the conclusion that $s_{sp} = 0.5s_p$, although the average of their experiments was $s_{sp} = 0.52s_p$.

We now know why the Guest law does not hold true when the principal stresses are different at the elastic limit. This limit is reached in torsion when $s_{sc} = 0.578s_0$, but then it drops to $s_{sp} = 0.5s_p$, and plastic flow becomes evident as soon as two principal stresses become equal.

Good evidence of the correctness of our thesis is also provided by the tests of Dr. Stanton, described in the first column of p. 286 of the same volume of *Engineering*.

Bailey † discusses the sudden yield of solid shafts and gives these values of the yield stresses:

Greatest shearing stress for pure bending $k = 12,500$ lb./sq. in.

Greatest shearing stress for pure torque $k = 12,600$ lb./sq. in.

More recently we read in the valuable investigation by Swift ‡ in the comment on his fig. 5:

" The shear relationship obtained in this way under tensile conditions invites direct comparison with the shear stress/strain relationship obtained under torsion, and such a comparison is made in fig. 5.

" Without pursuing this comparison into greater detail than is justified, it is clear that although the two curves *lie together in a general way*, they reveal certain systematic differences. Since similar differences have been shown by tests on another mild steel from which torsion specimens were bored out to tubular form, the results are considered as representative. The most significant points of difference are: The principal shear stresses at *initial yield* are not the same. According to the shear-strain energy hypothesis of elastic breakdown the

---

* *Engineering*, 15th Sept., 1916, p. 268.

† *Engineering*, 27th July, 1917, p. 81.

‡ *Engineering*, 20th Oct., 1939, p. 454, last column.

yield stress in simple shear should exceed the semi-yield stress in tension in the ratio $\sqrt{(4/3)}$. Actually, the ratio appears to be greater, but since small departures in linearity of the torque-twist curve would affect the figure for shear stress at torsional yield to a considerable extent, no great significance is attached to the discrepancy."

With his accurate instruments Prof. Smith has demonstrated in this test that also for solid bars the elastic breakdown occurs according to the law of Maxwell, and for further strain a good agreement between half of the true tensile stress and torsional shear stress is obtained, in agreement with Coulomb's law, and this is essential.

We now refer to the outstanding tests made in the Swiss laboratories of the Technical High School of Zürich by Ros and Eichinger.* If we take the average of the first whole set of 16 comparative tests we find with the notation used above, $s_{sc}/s_0 = 0.6$, $s_{sp}/s_p = 0.52$.

But if we omit the first row of tests which everybody will consider as out of range, then we find almost exactly $s_{sc}/s_0 = 0.58$, confirming Maxwell's law, and $s_{sp}/s_p = 0.5$, confirming Coulomb's law.

Recently P. W. Bridgeman † published a brilliant experimental investigation of the law for plastic flow enunciated in Chap. XIII.

The author had chosen an expensive, though not very accurate arrangement, yet his conclusion expressed in the summary before the article, and at the end, is not far amiss as he writes:

" Within the strain limits of this paper it is found that both the maximum shearing-stress criterion and the ' significant ' stress-strain criterion apply with errors of the order of 10 per cent, the maximum shearing-stress criterion being on the whole perhaps somewhat better."

We found that both criteria are fulfilled in their turn.

It would be unfair if we kept silent over some tests often quoted to deny the validity of Coulomb-Guest's law. There is no contradiction in the tests of Lode ‡; on the contrary, there is a confirmation of our conception since many points are situated on the ordinate $\mu = -1$. This is not the case with the results of Taylor and Quinney,§ who repeated Lode's tests. Our explanation of the fact that their diagram does not show these exceptional points is, that they probably rejected the results of tests which were too much out of the line they expected.

---

* *Versuche zur Klärung der Bruchgefahr*, III, " Metalle, Table I "; " Essais de Traction et de Compression ", " Essai de Torsion ", Rapport.

† Studies of plastic flow of steel, especially in two-dimensional compression. *Journal of Applied Physics*, Vol. 17, April, 1946, pp. 235–43.

‡ " Der Einfluss der mittleren Hauptspannung auf das Fliessen der Metallen Forschung ", Heft 303, 1928.

§ *Phil. Trans. Roy. Soc.*, Vol. 230, 1932, p. 323.

12. *The Graphical Construction of the Ideal Stress according to Maxwell's Law of Elastic Breakdown.*

In Chap. X, § 2, we found

$$\sqrt{s_1^2 + s_2^2 + s_3^2 + s_2 s_3 - s_3 s_1 - s_1 s_2} = s_0.$$

When the function of the principal stresses expressed in the first member of this equation remains below the yield limit s_0, we call

$$s_i = \sqrt{s_1^2 + s_2^2 + s_3^2 - s_2 s_3 - s_3 s_1 - s_1 s_2}$$

the ideal stress. This is a tension stress possessing the same safety margin to yield as the combined principal stresses.

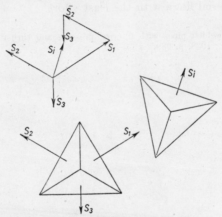

Fig. 131.—Construction of the ideal plastic stress
according to Meldahl

The graphical construction of s_i is the simplest imaginable as it consists of the vectorial addition at angles of 120° of the three principal stresses, as indicated at the top left of fig. 131.* There are several ways of proving the exactness of the construction. The proof by the following reasoning we consider most instructive.

To the left in the lower part of fig. 131 we have drawn the trihedral angle formed by half sides of the elementary cube (Chap. X, fig. 64) belonging to the three principal stresses. The plane of the drawing is a side of the octahedron. The problem is to construct a simple normal stress on a cube's side that gives the same shear stress on the sides

---

* A. Meldahl: *Brown Boveri Mitteilungen*, July–Aug., 1943, p. 204.

of the octahedron. As we have only to deal with the projections on the plane of the paper, the ideal stress obviously is s_i, and the trihedral angle shown at the right side of the figure indicates with its edges the principal directions belonging to this ideal stress. We invite the reader to apply the construction to test the validity of Maxwell's law for Palmer's test results,* and to explain why the agreement is unsatisfactory. By drawing three lines it can be proved that when the mean principal stress becomes equal to one of the extreme stresses, Maxwell's law and Coulomb's law concur.

This construction may also be used to illustrate clearly that for a given ideal stress the difference between the extreme principal stresses is smallest when the mean principal stress becomes equal to one of the extremes. If the stresses adjust themselves according to this condition, the material flows with the least effort.

* " Stresses in welded pipes with internal pressure and thrust or tension ", *Engineering*, 2nd Sept., 1938, p. 289.

CHAPTER XXIV

Plastic Flexure

The most striking experiment to show the reliability of the theory of elasticity for engineering practice, is the demonstration of the buckling load of flexure for a bar hinged at both ends, proving the exactness of Euler's formula $P = \dfrac{\pi^2}{l^2} EI$, in which $l =$ length of bar, $E =$ Young's modulus of elasticity, $I =$ moment of inertia of the section, $P =$ buckling load.

The agreement of calculated critical load with the experimental result is so good * that this laboratory test for which the author designed a simple apparatus, provides a good means to determine the modulus of elasticity for steel.

If we put $I = Ak^2$, A representing the area of the section and k the radius of gyration, and divide by A, we obtain the average buckling stress

$$p = \frac{P}{A} = \pi^2 \frac{k^2}{l^2} E.$$

We shall only discuss the flexure of bars of annealed mild steel. The yield pressure of this steel as delivered is very uncertain. By cold-straightening of the bars the yield point is raised. It also depends on the carbon content. For structural steel we shall take the yield point, i.e. the tension for plastic flow under compression, at $s_0 = 2020$ kg./cm.^{2} and the modulus of elasticity $E = 2{,}000{,}000$ kg./cm.^{2}, then if $l/k = 100$, we obtain $p = s_0$. We took these figures in order to obtain $l = 100k$, a ratio easily remembered for the limit of validity of Euler's formula of elastic flexure.

We repeat that the highest pressure consistent with elastic flexure is 2020 kg./cm.^{2} If we take shorter bars ($l < 100\,k$) Euler's formula would give a buckling stress exceeding the pressure for plastic flow. It is clear that such a load could not be carried and that the bar would

* Th. von Kármán: "Untersuchungen über Knickfestigkeit", *Dissertation Göttingen*, 1909; *Mitt. über Forschungsarb. a.d. Geb. des Ingenieurswesens*, Heft, 81, 1910.

collapse at an earlier stage. It is worth while to examine by experiment what happens when the compressed bars are shorter than 100k so that plastic flow occurs.

We shall not deny that the theoretical investigations made on this subject * are correct. But our tests were so arranged that the effect of the plasticity of the mild steel should be as pronounced as possible and we obtained results which will be a surprise to most students of applied mechanics. The reason for the difference from other people's experimental results † will be first explained. Other investigators tried columns made of cold-straightened material and obtained scattered results. We, however, followed the suggestion of Professor C. A. M. Smith of London University,‡ who wrote, "It is probable that the yield point of the material should be taken into account. It would, of course, be an advantage to use annealed specimens in all tests." We compared flexure and tension bars made of the same piece of iron, normalized at 900° C. for eight hours, and left to cool slowly in the oven. By this treatment we obtained material showing a distinct drop in resistance when the yield point was reached in the tension test. The results of the tests were as simple as possible. Our bars collapsed at the moment that the yield point was reached, and the deformation was permanent.

We now shall describe some of the tests made by M. G. Driessen,§ chief of the well-equipped mechanical research laboratories of the Netherlands State Mines.

The tests had to serve a practical purpose. For reasons of economy in the actual design of built-up columns, the material is concentrated at the periphery of the section. The tests were made with tubes, angle iron 30 × 30 × 4 mm., and with turned rods of 17 mm. diameter. For each series of three identical flexure tests, one test bar was drawn in order to determine the yield point of the material. The shape of the flexure as well as of the tension test bars is shown in fig. 132, and the bent strut in fig. 133.

The tests were made with different lengths l. But in order to secure plastic flexure, the slenderness $\lambda = l/k$ for the built-up section as well as for the section of each separate bar was made smaller than 100.

* Th. von Kármán, see above.

† S. Timoshenko, *Theory of Elastic Stability*, 1935, p. 45, " Bending beyond proportional limit ".

‡ *Engineering*, 1908, 21st Aug., p. 254, " The bending of columns under load ".

§ Ir. M. G. Driessen, *Knikproeven van constructies van samengestelde doorsnede met geringe slankheid*; *De Ingenieur*, 1934, No. 18, p. A 160.

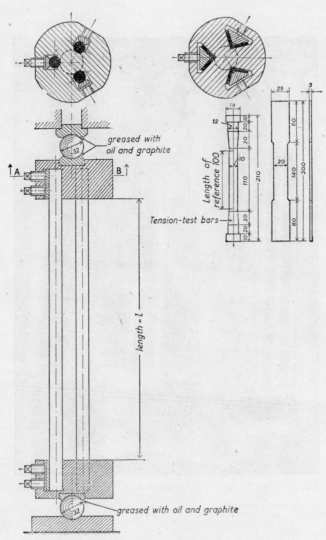

Fig. 132.—Arrangement for testing the flexural strength of built-up
columns and tension test bars

Fig. 133.—Test No. 10, three annealed rods flexed in Amsler testing machine

The results are given in the following table:

FLEXURE TESTS WITH SECTIONS BUILT UP FROM
THREE ANGLE IRONS 30 × 30 × 4 mm.

Test No.	Length l in mm.	Section cm.²	Buckling Load kg.	Buckling stress kg./cm.²	Tension test bar of same material		
					Section cm.²	Yield	
						Load kg.	Stress kg./cm.²
8	349	6·79	15320	2260	0·61	1300	2130
9	349	6·81	15850	2330	0·61	1340	2200
10	349	6·80	15100	2225	0·59	1390	2355
11	349	6·81	15500	2275	0·604	1400	2320
12	349	6·56	15900	2425	0·60	1380	2300
13a	127	6·55	16200	2475⎫	0·60	1415	2360
13b	127	6·54	16400	2505⎭			
14	349	6·55	16600	2535	0·587	1460	2485
15a	127	6·59	16500	2500⎫	0·603	1430	2370
15b	127	6·59	16700	2535⎭			
16	349	6·49	15500	2390	0·614	1460	2380
17a	127	6·53	16600	2540⎫	0·617	1460	2365
17b	126	6·52	16150	2480⎭			
FLEXURE TESTS WITH TURNED RODS 17 mm. DIA.							
8	349	6·77	16200	2390	0·777	1820	2340
9a	126	6·79	16400	2410⎫	0·777	1780	2290
9b	126	6·76	16400	2425⎭			
10	349	6·80	15600	2295	0·785	1980	2520

Some of these are represented graphically in figs. 134 and 135.

The bars for tests 8, 9, 10 and 11 were taken from one piece of angle iron, also the bars for tests 12, 13a and 13b, for 14, 15a and 15b, and for 16, 17a and 17b. All the tests with round turned bars were made with round iron taken from the same rod.

If from these tests the conclusion could be drawn that for columns built up from angle iron the buckling stress is a few per cent higher than the yield point, the contrary might be concluded for columns composed of round bars. On the average the tests provide a perfect confirmation of the law for plastic flexure:

buckling stress = yield point.

For columns or struts built up from bars of annealed mild steel with a definite drop in resistance when the yield point is reached and

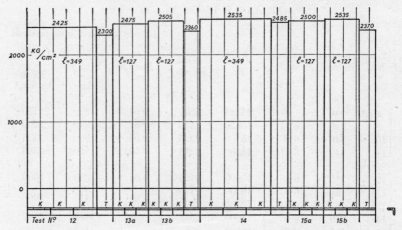

Fig. 134.—Buckling stress and yield point for annealed bars of different lengths composed of three angle irons. K denotes flexure test, T tension test, *l* length shown in fig. 132

with a slenderness $\lambda < 100$, the buckling stress is independent of the slenderness.

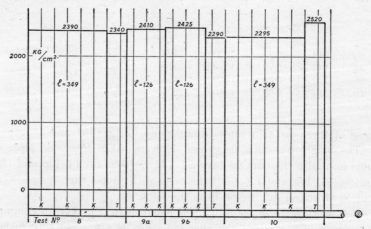

Fig. 135.—As fig. 134 but for three round rods (see fig. 133)

This conclusion is in disagreement with the general assumption which led to the empirical formulæ for column design.* But under

* S. Timoshenko: *Theory of Elastic Stability*, 1936, p. 183.

the conditions in which our tests were made the columns decidedly collapsed at the moment the yield point was reached. This is clearly indicated in fig. 136, showing the load diagrams for our experiments.

When we published this law for plastic flexure it gave rise to sharp controversy, and M. G. Driessen made a new series of tests.* The average of 31 tests was a manifest confirmation of the rule $p =$ buckling stress = yield point = s_0. The greatest deviations being $p/s_0 = 1\cdot07$ and $0\cdot92$, but generally p/s_0 was very near 1.

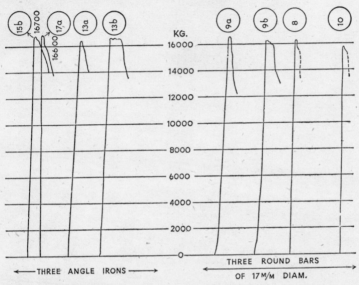

Fig. 136.—Compression diagrams for bars built up from three angle irons or three round rods

Driessen also experimented on the flexure of thin-walled tubes, and again found the law confirmed. Only when the very short tubes did not bend, but bulged, was there some deviation from the law.

The most conclusive confirmation of the law is supplied by large-scale tests using a very elaborate construction for the end supports of the columns in the Berlin-Dahlem Material-Testing Laboratory.†

Further information on the significance of the yield point in column tests may be obtained in Timoshenko's famous handbook.‡

* " Continuation of flexural tests with built-up columns of small slenderness ", *De Ingenieur*, 1934, No. 32, p. A 297.

† W. Rein: *Versuche zur Ermittlung der Knickspannungen für verschiedene Baustähle* (J. Springer, Berlin, 1930).

‡ Chapter III, " Experiments and Design Formulæ ".

INDEX

Admonton's law, 43, 62.
Airy's stress function, 4, 12, 18.
Amsterdam, High Pressure Laboratory, 30.
Autographic diagram, 78, 115.
Axial velocity at nozzle, 52.

Bach, 134.
Bader, 109.
Bailey, 159.
Bakelite, 123.
Ball test, 92.
Bending moment, 8.
—— critical, 8.
—— ideal, 79.
— stress, 8.
Biconical region, 128.
Bijlaard, 69.
Bleich, 9.
Bollenrath, 131.
Bollenrath and Schmied, 120.
Bridgeman, P. W., 160.
Brinell hardness test, 92.
Briquetting, 60.
Buckling load, 163.
— stress, 167, 168, 169.
Built-up columns, 165.
Bursting pressure, 11, 14.
Bylaard, P. P., 119.

Campus, F., 145.
Caratheodory and Schmidt, 59.
Cement, 134, 137.
Cementite, 5, 115.
Characteristic shearing stress, 64.
Chase, 155.
Clay, 32.
Clay-cutting, 59.
Clay, modelling, 155.

Cohesive forces, 65.
Cold-pressing, 123, 124.
— -rolling, 55.
— -straining, 137.
— -working, 21, 28, 115.
Colonetti, 9.
Compressed mass, outer regions of, 56.
Compression between inclined planes, 49.
—— parallel planes, 40.
Cone hardness test, 101.
— indentation, 101.
— truncated, 103, 130.
Congelation of soil, 13.
Contours, 111.
Cook, 11.
Cook and Robertson, 30.
Coulomb-Guest criterion or theorem, 70, 76, 78, 79, 80, 85, 108, 109, 121, 151, 158, 159, 160, 165.
Cracks, intercrystalline, 38.
Creep, 91.
Crushing strength, 23.
Crystallites, 125, 129.
Cup-shaped regions, 48, 88.
Cycloids, 19, 41, 47.
Cylinder, contracting, 154.
— thick-walled, 10.
— thin-walled, 152.
— translation of, 59.
— under internal pressure, 10.
— with rectangular boring, 33.
—— square boring, 26, 30.
—— triangular boring, 32.
Cylinders, annular space between, 59.

Deep indentation, 119.
Denoël, Lucien, 13.
De Saint Venant, B., 85, 131.

171

Dihedral angle, 49.
Drawing of metal, 124.
Driessen, M. G., 164, 169.
Drop shearing stress, 156, 157.
Ductility, 39.
Dutch State Mines, 36, 106, 122, 123.

Eichinger, 5
Elliptic co-ordinates, 141.
Elongation curve, 4.
Energy of distortion, 69.
Epicycloids, 59, 60.
Equilibrium, equations of, under internal stress, 4.
Etching-lines, 126.
Etching of polished sections, 7.
Euler's formula, 163.
Extruded band, equilibrium of, 45.
Extrusion, 51.

Ferrite 5, 121.
Flexure tests, 167.
Fokkinga, 122.
Fritsche, 4, 9.
Fry's liquor, 7, 21, 114, 115.

Gaskets, 47, 90.
— Armco iron, 47.
Geiringer and Prager, 124.
Geodetic survey, 111.
Griffith, A. A., 132.
Groove, rectangular, 106.
Grooved bars, 26.
— cylindrical test bar, 102.
Guest, 70, 158, 159, 160.

Hair crack, 104.
Hartmann lines, 115, 116, 117, 118, 119, 132.
Heap of sand, 110.
Hencky's theorem, 15, 16, 17, 44, 60, 68, 70, 81, 95, 158.
Herbert, 24.
High-speed tools, 24.
Huber-Hencky hypothesis, 68, 70, 78, 79, 80, 158.
Hypocycloids, 59, 60.

Ideal shear stress, 76.
— stress, graphical construction, 161.
— yield stress, 76.
Indentation by cone, 101.
— of curved surfaces, 146.
— tests, 100.

Joffé, 133.

Keyway, semicircular, 111.
— square, 111.
Kist, 9, 68.
Klopper, 71.
Knife-blade, 21.
Körber, 5.
Kronenberg, 24.
Kuntze, W., 105, 125.

Lacquer, 114.
Lamé, 13.
Lautal, 103.
L'Hermite, 9.
Liége, 130.
Lode, 160.
Logarithmic spirals, 13, 19.
Lubricants, unctuous, 60.
— viscous, 60.
Lubrication of surfaces, 61.
Lüder lines, 115, 117.
Ludwik, P., 8, 123.

Maier-Leibniz, 9.
Marble, 133.
Mariotte, 127, 128, 131, 135, 139, 140.
Maxwell's criterion, 68, 69, 70, 71, 76, 78, 85, 135, 136, 139, 156, 158, 159, 160, 161, 162.
Mayer, 99.
Mean principal stress, 83.
Meldahl's construction, 85, 161.
Membrane analogy, 112.
Mesmer, G., 101.
Metal-cutting, 23.
Michels, 30.
Mining, 138.
Mohr's stress circle, 2, 76, 118.
Möller and Barbers, 120.

Moment of inertia of section, 8.
Moulds for plastics, 123.

Nadai, A., 21, 36, 49, 103, 109, 114.
Navier's hypothesis 8.
Neck, conical, 78.
— cylindrical, 78.
Necking, 129.
Neuber, H., 141.
Neutral axis, 8.
— circle, 60.
— line, 8.
Non-deaerated clay, 60.
Non-plastified regions, 46.
Normalizing, 39.

Odguist and Schaub, 120.
Oxy-acetelene torch, 140.

Packing-ring, 90.
Palmer, 162.
Paste-spout, 54.
Penetration of triangular prism, 21.
Plastic, 85.
— flexure, 163.
— packing, 90, 91.
— regions at end of crack, 33, 34.
— sector, 15, 19.
Plasticity, criterion of, 4, 6, 67.
— three-dimensional, 63.
Plastification at corners of a square
    hole, 28.
Plastometer, 86, 92.
— Scott's, 86.
Polar caps, 60.
Poucelet, 127, 128, 131, 133, 134, 135,
    136, 138, 139, 140.
Prandtl, 19, 36, 41, 49, 92, 109.
Pressure under punch, 96.
— — — graphical treatment, 97.
Principal directions, 1.
— planes, 1.
— stresses, 1.

Rein, W., 169.
Rinagl, 120.
Robertson, 11.
Rock salt, 138.
Rolled beams, 9.

Ros and Eichinger, 68, 133, 134, 160.
Rotating drum, 152.
Rounding of notch, 148.
Rumford, 25.
Rupture, 124.
— angle of, 119.
— at sharp incisions, 139.
— brittle, 123, 125, 130, 131.
— cone-and-cup, 122, 130.
— criterion for, 64.
— stress, 122.
— theory of, 131, 133.

Sadowski, M. A., 112, 124.
Safety factor, 8, 76.
Sand-heap analogy, 112.
Saurin, N. N., 25.
Schaar, 131.
Schoenmaker, 128.
Scott, J. R., 86.
Sharp grooves, 26.
Sheet-metal rolling, 55.
Shurkow, 132.
Siebel and Vieregge, 120.
Siemens-Martin steel, 123.
Skoda works, 25.
Slate, 138.
Slenderness ratio, 164, 168.
Slip lines, 7, 13.
— planes, 113.
Smith, C. A. M., 10, 80, 158, 160, 164.
Soap-film, 110.
Specific deformation, 31.
— elongation, 67.
— — axis of octahedron, 73.
— — diagonal of cube, 72.
Square hole, 149.
— section with square boring, 31, 32.
Stanton, 159.
Stress, three-dimensional, general case,
    72.
Stress circle, 6, 15, 16, 42.
— heap, 109.
Stresses near re-entrant angle, 27.
— on elementary octahedron, 63.
— — — tetrahedron, 63.
Stress-strain diagram, 5.
Strip with shallow grooves, 35.
Stromeyer, 68.

Surface tension of molten iron, 38.
Swift, H. W., 9, 124, 153.

Taylor and Quinney, 160.
Tempering colour, 24.
Thick-walled sphere, 81.
Thum and Wunderlich, 104, 105, 120, 126.
Timoshenko, S., 134, 168, 169.
Tool friction, 23.
Torsion, plastic, 109.
Torsional stress heap, 110.
Trajectories of maximum shear stress, 13, 15, 19.
Tresca, H., 6, 55, 85.
Tummers, W. G. E., 30, 123.
Twisting moment, 79.

Unckel, H., 54.
Upper yield limit, 5.

van der Willigen, 128.
van Iterson, F., 10.
Varnish, 114.
Vening Meinesz, F. A., 119.
von Kármán, 133, 163.
von Mises, 68, 70.

Wedge, blunt, 20.
— loaded, 153.
Wire-drawing, 82.
Work-hardening, 24, 32, 39, 62, 99, 121, 127, 129, 137.
Wunderlich, 104, 105.